W9-BXQ-149

Twelve Mindful Months

Cultivating a Balanced & Fit Body, Mind & Spirit

Carol

Carol Tibbetts

Photography by the author

TRUE NATURE PRESS

Published by
True Nature Press
Box 553
Solana Beach, CA 92075-0553
www.truenaturepress.com

Twelve Mindful Months:
Cultivating a Balanced & Fit Body, Mind & Spirit

Cover design, interior design/typesetting by Teri Rider

Printed in the U.S.A.

Library of Congress Control Number: 2012947872
ISBN Number: 978-0-615-68758-2

First Edition

CONTENTS

Introduction

INTRODUCTION

Most women who are health-minded share similar goals: To look and feel their best, and to be able to manage stress. Many of you may have tried all kinds of fitness fads and diets with either no success, or success that doesn't last. You may eat healthy foods and exercise, but still cannot manage stress. Or maybe you are a fitness fanatic, but you mindlessly fuel your body on junk food. This book makes the achievement of life-long healthy habits possible by addressing the most common ingredient missing from most people's wellness endeavors: mindfulness.

Mindfulness is the process of being present with your surroundings and with what you are doing and feeling. When you are mindful you experience more contentment and are satisfied with less. When you are unmindful you lose control over your actions and become reactive. If you remain present and fully aware you will make healthier choices. By becoming more mindful, you will gain an understanding of how your body and mind work, why your wellness attempts failed or succeeded in the past, and how you got off – or stayed on – track. If you do not understand yourself or your habits, not even the best trainer will motivate you. Creating a balance of body, mind, and spirit is the key to making permanent lifestyle changes. *Twelve Mindful Months…* will show you month by month, practical ways to integrate exercise, healthy eating, and mindfulness into your days to develop life-long habits to achieve that balance.

Throughout my three-decade fitness career, I have seen firsthand how periods of stress, the natural cycles of life, and seasonal influences can interfere with clients' healthy intentions and progress. While there are no shortcuts to fitness, weight loss, or mindfulness, this book can help you find and stay on a healthy path; especially when you encounter potholes and speed bumps along the way.

Twelve Mindful Months… will also show you how you can attain mind/body balance by adapting to the flow of the seasons and nature. Connecting to nature and the environment is essential to our well-being. Although we are instinctively drawn to the peace and harmony of nature during difficult times, many of us tend to spend too little time outside, or ignore it in the daily rush of our overscheduled lives. All of the photographs in this book were captured by me on walks outdoors, to inspire awareness and appreciation for the simple beauty found in the imperfection of nature. *Twelve Mindful Months…* will reconnect you to the outside world and help you discover your true nature, as you cultivate a balanced and fit body, mind and spirit.

Namasté,

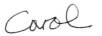

HOW TO USE THIS BOOK

Twelve Mindful Months... is designed to teach you how to incorporate simple concepts of exercise, healthy eating and mindfulness into your daily routine, month by month.

Although this book begins with the month of January, you can start wherever you are right now, in the present month. Each chapter introduces a nature or seasonal theme and includes three related tips for fitness activities, healthy eating, and mindfulness. Choose at least one tip from each category to integrate into your life each month. Studies have shown that new habits are more likely to become life-long practices when only one change is made at a time. Photocopy the weekly activity and healthy eating logs which are included at the end of this book, (or download the free PDF version which is located on the "Resources" page of the True Nature Press website: www.truenaturepress.com), so you can record your daily exercise activity and food intake, and note progress. Use the journal pages provided at the end of each month to explore the monthly journaling prompt or to write about your feelings and experiences. Proceed the same way for each month thereafter. As you incorporate new tips from each chapter, keep practicing the ones you've already added, and soon they will become second nature.

The cycle of nature teaches us that each new day brings the opportunity to see new in the old. And as we observe the seasonal changes in nature, we are better able to accept each season of our life, enabling us to live freely in the present. If you follow the simple steps in this book, next year you will be content where you are, finding joy in each moment, while moving mindfully toward your future.

Enjoy the journey!

January

JANUARY
Rejuvenation Resolution

"Within you there is a stillness and sanctuary to which you can retreat at any time and be yourself." Hermann Hesse

New Year's Resolutions. We've all made them at least once in our lifetime – those overly optimistic diet and exercise goals that we are only able to follow for a month or two at the most. Despite high motivation, often times unanticipated family, work, or household obligations get in the way and foil our best intentions. The main reason we fail to keep our resolutions is because our plan to exercise more or eat healthier is based on our "ideal" life – not the one we really live, where kids get the flu, the furnace breaks down, and work deadlines pop up out of nowhere. While there may be legitimate times when you have to skip your exercise routine, we often use time or conflicts as an excuse, when better planning could have prevented our exercise derailment. It's easy to use time as a reason because it takes the blame off ourselves and puts it elsewhere. When we are truly motivated – and mindful – we are strong enough and aware enough to stick to our goals. This month we will explore ways that will help us avoid going down the same paths that derailed us in the past.

Start the year by reflecting on all you did to benefit your body, mind, and spirit in the past year, and see whether there are any opportunities for improvement. Set realistic goals based on these discoveries that will allow you to live joyfully in the now while moving mindfully into the future. Perhaps your intention is just to maintain the healthy routines you've already been doing or to be more consistent in carving out time for daily exercise. Consult a fitness trainer to help you design a specific plan of action as to how you will achieve these goals and where you'd like to be 3, 6, and 12 months from now. Writing down goals helps solidify them, but no matter how good a plan you have, you must keep an open mind, anticipate roadblocks, and be flexible to change if you are to achieve success.

As you set new goals this January, consider how to work within the bounds of nature. Perhaps one reason why we often fail to stick with our New Year's Resolutions is because we are going against the natural cycle of the winter season. As growing, living beings we are just as much a part of nature as the trees, plants, and animals. Every perennial garden has an annual cycle: It germinates, grows, and flowers during spring and summer, then dies and retreats during winter to gather energy to bloom again next year. We humans also need a time to honor nature's cycle of rest and **rejuvenation.** This doesn't mean hibernating inside all winter eating chips and watching TV. Instead, use this month to turn your thoughts inward and contemplate how you can de-stress and create a balanced body, life, and spirit by making a **resolution** to slow down and synchronize with the natural forces at play.

Think yin instead of yang. If you are someone who works out hard all year, skip the gym for a month and go for walks or light jogs or trade power yoga for a restorative class. If you are someone who last year let work get in the way of your healthy intentions, take the time now to anticipate upcoming job challenges and formulate a plan to cope that will keep you on track. Make time for exercise through careful planning of your schedule and create space within each day to be alone. When life interrupts your plans, go for a short walk or do a few sun salutations (or other yoga poses) to keep you on the wellness track and off the "all-or-nothing" madness track. If you suffer from "activity addiction," seek more relaxing past-times like reading, knitting, or artistic pursuits to keep you busy and challenged in a less competitive way. Consider going to a spa or taking a silent retreat: a week, a weekend, a day or just an hour alone to connect with your inner self and rejuvenate your reserves. By slowing down and creating calmness, you will actually be bolstering your intention to exercise because you will become more mindful of what your body needs and who and what influences your daily decisions and habits.

Modern society is addicted to stimulus, but our souls yearn for silence. Even just 10 minutes of silence can renew your energy and spirit. Try to spend an entire day driving in your car without using your cell phone or playing music. Notice how often you automatically have an urge to fill the space with sound, or to multi-task. If you always exercise with music, disconnect from your iPod for one workout, and tune in to the melody of your own breath. If you are someone who constantly reads and sends text messages or emails, consider checking them only at the beginning of each hour, or set a limit of no more than three times a day. Learn how to be comfortable with your own thoughts, and appreciate the freedom that comes from being still and in the present.

Take this month to follow nature's lead. Experience the silence and stillness of January. Allow yourself time to slow down, to pamper your soul and spirit, so you can experience energy **rejuvenation**. Although winter can be a depressing season due to diminished sunlight, it is a much needed time of hibernation for all of us. Winter reminds us that life changes and someday we, too, will be in the winter of our life. Restore yourself in January so you will have renewed energy for the next cycle of life that awaits you. Say "no" to old New Year's **resolutions,** and resolve to evolve.

Fitness Tips:

- **Snow Conundrum:** If you live in a cold climate, stay home whenever possible when it snows. A snowstorm is nature's way of getting us to slow down. Rather than taking a risky drive to the gym, shovel snow for exercise, snowshoe or ski, or go for a walk. Trudging through heavy snow increases the work load on the legs and heart, burning more calories than on a treadmill or dry road. If icy surfaces keep you inside, invest in a pair of ice cleats that you can stretch over your shoes or boots to increase safety and traction. Revive your childhood joy of snow while connecting with nature: Even if you don't have kids to play with, make a snow angel, build a snowman, throw some snowballs, or go sledding. All of these snowy pursuits are fun ways to exercise and de-stress, and allow you to connect to your inner child. And if you don't live in a cold climate, create yin (slow, quiet) days filled with walks in nature or restorative yoga, T'ai Chi, or gentle stretches to safeguard your energy reserves.

- **Don't Hurry – Be Happy:** If you are just beginning or resuming an exercise program, it's important to build a base of fitness slowly. Having a strong foundation to draw from will help you stay steady with your intentions and prevent injury and setbacks. When taking up a new sport or class (like yoga), be patient with your progress; the most important factor is that you're doing it. Stay present within your own body and mind, and resist the urge to compare yourself to others. We all were beginners once, and to choose not to try something new for fear of looking uncoordinated is to not fully live and experience life. By conquering our small fears and experiencing a beginner's mind, we can remain humble and compassionate while practicing confidence for life's bigger challenges. Enjoy the journey so you can fully appreciate the progress toward your future.

- **Mindful Yin/Yang Cardio:** If you are someone who prefers structure, follow a weekly cardio plan that alternates yang (hard) workouts, like high-intensity interval training, with yin (easy) workouts, like long slower walks or runs, to rev up metabolism, build a stronger heart and lungs, and prevent over-training injuries and burnout. Incorporating yin and yang workouts will help you stay mindful of your energy level and how your body feels, while encouraging exercise compliance and respecting the body's need for recovery workouts alternated with high intensity. If your goal is to simply rejuvenate your reserves this month (or if you haven't been exercising regularly at least 3 months), perform only yin workouts, and try to do them outdoors as often as possible. If you feel tempted to skip the gym after a long day at work, having a choice of a yin workout will allow you to stay on track with your intentions while you unwind in a healthy way.

HEALTHY EATING TIPS:

- **Breakfast Club:** If you have yet to join the "Breakfast Club," it's high time you did. Nutritionists agree that breakfast is an essential part of a healthy diet and any successful weight loss program. And contrary to popular belief, you burn more calories (and have more energy) when you eat a *small* meal before your morning workout. Just like your morning shot of caffeine helps you wake up, food in the morning awakens your metabolism, which has been in low gear all night. A bowl of whole-grain, high-fiber, low-fat, low-sugar cereal with fruit and 1% milk provides carbs, protein, and minimal fat, and is an easy way to get a third to half the fiber you need for the day. If you just can't face traditional breakfast foods, try healthy alternatives, such as Greek yogurt with berries; peanut butter and banana; or low-fat cheese and tomato on toasted whole-grain bread. Winter is the perfect time of year for hot oatmeal, an important grain that has been proven to help reduce the absorption of "bad" (LDL) cholesterol into the bloodstream. (Cook it with milk instead of water for added protein and calcium.) Add chopped walnuts and apple slices, dust with cinnamon, drizzle with a little honey – and oatmeal may have you saying "yes" to breakfast.

- **Swap Out:** To help you stick to newly acquired healthy food choices, modify only one eating habit at a time. Swap white pasta for whole grain, replace your full-fat latte for skinny, or choose fruit instead of cookies for dessert. If there are many dietary changes you'd like to make this year, compose a list and check off one new switch per month, beginning with the easiest one first. And don't be hard on yourself: Allow yourself one time per week NOT to swap, at least for this month. Having a choice will help your realize you really do prefer the healthier alternative now.

- **Dieter's Remorse:** Practice being more mindful to avoid dieter's remorse: Research has shown that focusing on the *anticipation* of remorse helps subjects stay committed to their healthy intentions. Try this the next time you're tempted to grab a scone at Starbucks (450 calories) or to order fries instead of a salad. Ask yourself: "How will I feel tomorrow about the decision I made today?" Above all, practice self-compassion. Remember that the best of intentions sometimes do fail; let go of the need to always be perfect. Your good intention was there, and tomorrow is another day. Research has also shown that people who are more self-compassionate are more likely to stay with their intentions and create life-long habits.

MINDFULNESS TIPS:

- **Isolation Strategy:** As we age, getting out to socialize requires more effort than it did in our youth, and it can be tempting to decline social engagements. If you live alone or work from your home, say "yes" as often as you can, and you will experience more joy in your life. If you feel isolated, make a list of activities you could do with others, groups you could be a part of, and people with whom you would like to connect. Also, consider ways to meet people who are not your age – older and younger generations – to help broaden your worldview. Then make a call or plan to get out to a meeting, show, meal, or class at least once a week.

- **Healthy Hibernation:** If, on the other hand, a hectic social calendar is the norm for you, keep social commitments to a minimum this month. Learn to say "no" to unnecessary events. Rejuvenate your reserves by spending more time at home. Walk outdoors on a moonlit night. If you live in the North, observe the tree branches encased in icy shells, which allows them to draw their energy reserves inward. Notice the ambient sounds that surround you. Observe the quietness of nature as you observe the quietness of your own mind. Keep the memory of these peaceful moments alive in your mind to help you relax at times when you cannot be alone or in nature and have feelings of stress, fear, or anger.

- **Creativity Journal:** Journaling doesn't have to be limited to just writing. Allow your inner artistic self to come out and play. Get creative. Doodle or sketch, use colored pens or ink stamps, or cut and paste images or letters from magazines.  Compose a poem, a haiku, or a song. It's about the process, not the result, so avoid critiquing your own work. Create a vision board of your future intentions, make a collage portraying all your personal strengths, or the "inner you" you'd like to reveal to the world. You might discover an image that feeds your soul. Creative journaling gives your soul a voice, guiding you in your journey of self-discovery, to help you find your life purpose, as it **rejuvenates** your spirit, brightening even the darkest days of winter.

JAN

JOURNAL

JOURNAL

February

FEBRUARY

Love Your Heart / Love Your Body

"The kind of beauty I want most is the hard-to-get kind that comes from within—strength, courage, dignity." RUBY DEE

February is National Heart Health Month, dovetailing nicely with Valentine's Day, an occasion when we express appreciation towards those we love, often with heart-shaped symbols. Heart disease – not cancer – is the leading cause of death in women, yet many women worry more about getting breast cancer than having a heart attack. This month's focus is on exercising and eating for a healthy heart, and features mindful techniques to help you learn how to appreciate and love your heart *and* your body.

The heart is our life force and yet we often take its continual pumping for granted. Some people pay more attention to the upkeep of their cars than their bodies. Take this month to be aware of what you fuel your body with, and you will feel less like filling yourself with fatty foods or sugar, which clog your engine and slow you down. And to maintain a strong and healthy heart, aim for at least three 30 - 60 minute cardiovascular workouts of moderate-to-hard intensity each week, along with (as recommended by the American College of Sports Medicine (ACSM)), a minimum of one weekly session of a mind/body activity, like yoga, T'ai Chi, or meditation.

Many of us may already maintain our hearts with aerobic exercise and a healthy diet, but have neglected to find time to reduce stress – a major risk factor for heart attacks. Chronic emotional stress elevates blood pressure and causes plaque to build up twice as fast in the coronary arteries, reducing blood flow to the heart and increasing the risk of blood clots that can cause a heart attack. Ironically, it is not the occasional major stressful events that are most damaging, but rather the small stressors we deal with day to day, all year.

Stress abounds in life, but if you learn how to manage it with relaxation techniques, your heart will be healthier. Many women are more concerned with burning calories, and therefore always choose cardio over mind/body activities, claiming it relaxes them. While it's true that aerobic exercise does help release stress, it doesn't teach you how to release stress the other 23 hours of the day when you're not doing cardio.

The breath awareness and focusing techniques used in meditation, yoga, and T'ai Chi classes can easily be adapted for life practice. In addition to the physical poses, yoga teaches breath awareness and how to calm the mind, skills we need to navigate the frenetic treadmill of life. Research suggests that even 5 minutes of meditation or yoga every day can decrease stress by helping to diffuse emotions such as anger, hostility, and impatience that increase heart attack risk. Find a style of yoga or a T'ai Chi class that suits your body and current ability, a teacher you like, and attend at least one (or three if you can) sessions per week.

We send heart-felt love to others each Valentine's Day. But how often do we send love to ourselves? Learning to accept our bodies – the strengths *and* flaws – is an essential ingredient for a less anxious life, and without it, we will never be at peace. Popular culture leads us to believe that happiness and being loved depend on having an ageless and perfect body. As more and more women succumb to this pressure, they stress their hearts either from lack of adequate nutrition, too many elective cosmetic surgeries, or the mental anguish of their desperation to achieve the "perfect" weight. On the other hand, more than half of the American population is overweight, and if you are one of them you *should* be concerned about your weight, since you have increased risk of heart disease, diabetes, and some cancers. Strive to achieve your healthy ideal weight: even a 10% weight loss will improve your health. However, if you are already at a healthy weight but continually obsess over losing the "last 10 pounds" – or feel driven to be a size 6, 4, 2 or 0 – you may want to question your motives and the likelihood of attaining your goal. Instead, set reasonable goals based on your body type, genetics, and age to improve your chance of succeeding.

As we build compassion for ourselves, we build compassion for others, and our capacity to love increases. You've heard the adage that "you have to be a friend to have a friend." The same logic applies to your ability to give and receive love. A healthy, loving relationship with a significant other starts with the respect and love you have toward yourself. Send gratitude every day to your body, and you will learn to love even those parts you want to change. Instead of wishing your thighs were smaller, thank them for being strong and able to support you on your walk or run. Show your love and gratitude for your legs by massaging them lovingly with your favorite moisturizer. With practice, you can learn to find joy in your own skin. Happiness is fleeting and dependent on external events or material things, whereas true joy is not. Practicing appreciation for your life and what your body *can* do will allow you to find joy in your heart – which ultimately triggers the desire to give your body the physical care it needs. Love your body and accept it as it is, with all its flaws and all its beauty. **Love your heart/love your body**.

FITNESS TIPS:

- **Have a Heart:** There is gain without pain. Don't subscribe to the outdated notion that exercise must hurt to be effective. Be fully present in your body as you exercise so you can differentiate between a dull, aching sensation (which is often how people describe muscle fatigue or a full stretch) and a sharp, stabbing sensation that signifies "immediately stop what you're doing." Know your "edge" in yoga (i.e., that place in a stretch where you begin to feel something happening), and resist the urge to push any farther. Go to the point of muscle fatigue as you strength train, as long as you can maintain good form. In cardio, strive for a comfortably challenging intensity level most days. Be aware of signs of over-exertion. Dizziness, lightheadedness, and nausea are signs the body is working too hard. Be aware so you can *be*ware. Treat yourself with compassion, and do no harm as you care for your body.

- **Choose to Move:** The heart is your most important muscle. Show your love by being active at least 30 minutes daily. And then find ways to move more often throughout the day. The hours you sit in a chair increase your risk of dying, even if you exercise an hour per day. We utilize five times more oxygen walking slowly than sitting, and ten times more when walking fast. Remember, movement does not have to be continuous (you can walk 15 minutes two times or 10 minutes three times, per day). To remind yourself to move more, wear a pedometer and try to achieve a daily average of 10,000 steps or a weekly total of 70,000. To improve performance and strength-train your heart, work at a challenging intensity for a minimum of 20 continuous minutes at least three times per week. Daily aerobic exercise has been proven to increase the "good" (HDL) blood cholesterol level, whereas sitting too long causes these levels to drop.

- **Build Better Body Appreciation:** With each step you take, visualize your heart getting stronger and healthier. With each breath you take, imagine healing energy entering your body, and with each exhalation, imagine stress going out. At the end of your workout, send gratitude and appreciation to your heart, lungs, and legs for what you were able to accomplish. Be aware of any tendency to judge or berate yourself for not performing well. Instead of negative self-talk, build body contentment by reminding yourself of all your strengths. If you don't know how to be content in your mind, you will never be content with anything or anyone else. A mind that is content is more able to appreciate.

Healthy Eating Tips:

- **Eat Heartily:**

1. **Embrace Omega-3 Fats:** Consume foods high in omega-3 fatty acids to improve heart health: Eat two weekly servings of salmon, tuna, walnuts, or ground flaxseeds. (Note: When adding flaxseeds, water intake should be upped.) To increase "good" (HDL) cholesterol levels, use heart-healthy fats, such as olive oil, avocados, and walnuts. Limit saturated fats, like red meat, full fat cheeses, and butter which increase "bad" (LDL) cholesterol levels.

2. **Eat Outside the Box:** Avoid or limit foods that you eat out of a box or can. Leading nutrition groups report that 80% of our sodium intake is hidden in processed and prepared foods, while only 11% comes from what we add from the salt shaker. Lower your salt intake (and your blood pressure) by buying low-sodium foods, using oil and vinegar instead of bottled salad dressings, and cooking more at home, since restaurant meals can have ten times the recommended daily amount of salt, in just one entrée. When cooking, add flavor by substituting dried herbs like basil or oregano (which are also high in antioxidants) in place of salt. The recommended intake for added sodium for adults who are over age 50, overweight, have high blood pressure, or are salt sensitive is no more than 1,500 milligrams (mg) per day (a little more than half a teaspoon of regular table salt). If you're like most Americans, your salt consumption is probably six to eight times that amount. Cut your sodium down just ½ teaspoon (1,000 mgs) per day, and you will significantly decrease your risk of heart attack, stroke, and cancer.

- **Mindful Weigh-ins:** Weight is not the measure of your worth. Reframe your results-oriented goals (i.e., numbers on the scale) to make your journey more joyful. Skip daily weigh-ins, which can be more indicative of fluid gain/loss than true pounds added or dropped. Instead, weigh yourself on Fridays and Mondays, to keep you in check over the weekend. If you must weigh-in, realize its how you feel and how healthy a week you had that is most important. Have a trainer test your body fat to determine an appropriate goal.

- **Think Red:** (Produce – not meat!) This month love your heart by incorporating more *red* veggies and fruits into your diet. Try adding red kidney beans (high in protein and fiber), dried cherries, pomegranates, red grapes, beets, and red peppers, all of which contain powerful antioxidants. And don't forget tomatoes; they are high in potassium, which helps keep blood pressure in check.

MINDFULNESS TIPS:

- **Add Serenity Breaks:**

  1. **Unplug:** Take a break from chatter. Consider adopting silent Sundays – or at least unplug as much as you can – to honor our winter need for more solitude.

  2. **Relax:** Once a day (or at least weekly), take time for your favorite hobby, to read, or to just relax or have fun, all proven methods of lowering blood pressure. Indulge in a hot bath, and as you bathe, soap yourself with the same tenderness you would give a child.

  3. **Meditate:** Practice a spa ritual and choose a daily time to meditate: Set a timer for 10 to 20 minutes. Sit upright with good posture in a comfortable position on

the floor (or in a chair with your feet flat), hands relaxed, palms turned upward on your thighs. Close your eyes and focus on your breathing (the in and the out) and count each breath cycle. After three cycles, go back to number one, and begin counting again. Acknowledge any thoughts that arise (and they will), and then refocus on your breath. Performing a de-stressing ritual at the same time each day will help your body and mind unwind more easily as they adapt to the new pattern.

- **Restore and Renew:** Practice being kind to yourself. Take a weekly restorative yoga class, or practice a sequence of calming, longer-held stretches on your own. Gentle reclining and seated postures (which allow you to relax more than standing postures) counteract many stress-related negative by-products of our fast-paced, high-output lives. Soothing stretches activate the part of the nervous system that slows you down, lowering heart rate and normalizing blood pressure. As your muscles learn to relax and release, it increases your depth of self-awareness and compassion. Try this simple restorative yoga posture: Lie on your back and bring your legs up on a wall. Close your eyes and relax, with palms turned down on your lower abdomen or with arms by your side and palms up. This posture is extremely beneficial for restoring energy and reducing fluid build-up in the legs and feet after a long plane flight or after a busy day on your feet.

- **Journal of Love:** Do you "love what you do" and "do what you love?" Does your vocation make you feel whole? Despite successful careers and all the things money can buy, you will remain unfulfilled if you have not found your soul's purpose. You know if you have found your true purpose in life when your work or favorite pastime makes you feel both peaceful and exhilarated. If you have not found your life purpose yet, it is there deep within you, awaiting discovery. Meditation and yoga will help you find it, if you focus on that intention and listen to the wisdom of your heart. Use a journal to explore feelings and ask questions of yourself and your life. What makes your heart sing? When engaged with doing what you love, what impact does it have on others? How does it impact you later? Write about a time in your life when you felt loved and appreciated, or express the love you feel for someone else or even a pet. What qualities of this love come from within you, and what do you give back? Design a valentine card for yourself, and send personal messages of love to your body. Get creative and use hearts, arrows, and even those fancy lace paper doilies you used in grade school. Place the card in your journal, or make it a separate page where you can see it and remind yourself of all there is to love about you, and your body.

Journal

_____

_____

_____

_____

_____

_____

_____

_____

_____

_____

_____

_____

_____

_____

_____

_____

JOURNAL

March

MARCH
Self-Reflection Leads to Transcendence

"Muddy water, let stand, becomes clear.
Do you have the patience to wait until your mind settles and
the water is clear?" Lao-Tzu

March ushers in the mud season in many places, so in this month of slow transition from winter, let's think about un-muddying our minds of negativity as we await the purifying arrival of spring and the promise of growth it can bring. To transcend negative behavior we must start by being present as often as possible. Listen to your inner messages: Compare those negative voices in your head with those positive voices from your heart center, where the soul resides. Which voice is louder? Sometimes positive self-talk can't be heard because our minds are too muddied with negativity or mindless chatter. Try gazing into a muddy pond: You can't see to the bottom, you see only what's on the surface. Through the process of self-awareness, we can learn to filter out the dirt of negative emotions so we can see more clearly. Control of our thoughts, or "cognitive over-ride," leads to control of our actions, which creates personal power. When you notice a negative thought come into your head ("I'll never learn to like exercise"), practice cognitive over-ride and delete it, pasting a positive thought in its place ("I *will* find some exercise I enjoy"). And listen more carefully for the whispers of your soul, by paying close attention to your breath and heart center. If you feel frustrated with your fitness and wellness attempts, practicing **self-reflection** and positive thinking can help **transcend** habitual thinking and develop a calmer attitude.

One of the most powerful tools we possess is self-reflection; that is learning from past experiences. It can be the key to behavioral change. Contemplate your past attempts at a fitness regime or diet plan. Many people repeat the same routines that failed in the past over and over again, hoping for a different outcome, which rarely happens. Instead, focus on past successes/failures and why they may/may not have worked. Were you motivated because of a trainer or teacher, or did you find joy in a class that continually provided variety, fun, and challenges? Or did you lose motivation because the workouts became predictable and boring, or the trainer wouldn't stop talking about himself? If past attempts were failures, was it because you forced yourself to get up early every morning to exercise before work, even though you are a night owl? Or were your efforts successful because you allowed yourself 3 days per week to sleep in, avoiding the "all-or-nothing" trap? Have you restricted food groups, starved yourself, or thought you had to eat perfectly all the time, only to revert to binging all weekend until Monday, when you tried the same tactic again? If you don't understand *why* you failed or succeeded in the past, no amount of motivation will help you.

Resilience is a trait found in nature, and it's also a common characteristic of successful people. A tree shows its resilience after a long cold winter when it is able to grow new branches where old ones were broken off. Reflect on whether you have that ability to bounce back and the times you've used it. Learn to build up your own resilience by focusing on the upside of each challenge. The more hopeful you feel about your latest attempt or setback from an illness or injury, the more likely you'll be able to stick with it and bounce back. For example, instead of focusing on the frustration you feel for not being able to do your normal run because of a knee injury or newly diagnosed arthritis, focus on what you *can* do, such as biking, swimming, upper body, or core work. Less resilient people when sidelined tend to forgo all exercise, giving into anger, frustration, higher stress levels, and weight gain. Talk to your doctor about the specifics of what you can and cannot do, and formulate a time table of when you can add more. Even after major surgery, light daily walks are often recommended as soon as possible. Above all, practice gratitude for all you can do, and have done.

Research has shown that cardiovascular workouts improve brain function, due to the increased blood and oxygen flow. So, aerobic exercise, along with learning new skills and information, will help keep our brains agile as we age. And we can use this agility to train our brains to think differently and to transcend our habitual way of thinking. Neuroplasticity is the proven ability of the brain to change, adapt, and even rewire itself based on a new experience. Meditate on, or write and repeat positive affirmations or changes in thinking that you wish to manifest in your life. It's a lot like memorizing for a test: At first you may not fully understand or believe your new thoughts, but once the subconscious absorbs them, you will be able to fully embrace them. It takes practice to create new pathways, but that's what creates patterns that you eventually won't have to consciously think about. And with repetition, all positive thoughts and practice become deeper and more powerful over time.

So in this month of the vernal equinox – the first stage of transition from the dark of winter to the light of spring – un-muddy your mind from negativity and thoughts that no longer apply – and **transcend** to a more enlightened you. Through **self-reflection** you can make sense of your experiences, explore new self-beliefs, and alter your thinking and behavior. Take time to self-reflect, and you will enjoy renewed motivation to make the changes you most wish to see.

Fitness Tips:

- **Lion or Lamb:** Should your workouts roar like a lion or be gentle as a lamb? Be flexible and willing to adjust your weekly exercise schedule to what your body needs daily. If it's supposed to be your high-intensity day and you feel sore or tired, give yourself permission (guilt-free) to perform an easier "recovery" workout. (Do consider that sometimes it might be just your mind feeling lazy, and once you start exercising, you may feel better or more energetic.) Mindfulness leads to getting to know your body and trusting what it's telling you, so you can learn the difference between true pain (when you should stop) and mild discomfort. Body aches, fever, the flu, or chest congestion are signs that you should take a few days off, as exercise will make symptoms worse. If you have had an injury in the past, recall how cautious you were of every move even after you healed because of fear of re-injury or pain, and try to be more aware of where and how you place your feet, hands, and body in space. Whether you're doing cardio, weights, or yoga, *be* there. Be inside your body. Be mindful of what feels good and what does not.

- **Mind Your Muscles:** After age 40, women tend to lose muscle (lean body mass) two to three times faster than men. In addition to loss of strength and tone, less muscle mass slows metabolism, decreases bone density, and eventually causes balance problems and a reduced ability to perform functional daily activities. The proper exercise intensity is the key to getting results. Many women worry about getting too "bulky" from strength training and believe it is best to use light weights and high repetitions. However, the better, more effective way to build muscle is to use *heavier* weights and *fewer* repetitions. Select weights or resistance bands that are challenging enough that you can only complete 8 to 12 repetitions of each exercise. Perform two to three sets each, resting 20 to 30 seconds between. Include at least 1.5 to 2 hours of strength training each week to preserve healthy bones and muscles. Consult a personal trainer for optimal results and guidance, especially if you are just beginning. Not all strength training programs are created equal. A good trainer will evaluate your strengths and weaknesses and design a program based on them, along with your health history and lifestyle considerations.

- **Brain-Train for Success:** We're all familiar with the power of positive thinking. Do you practice it? You are – and you will become – what you think. If you can believe it, you can become it. If you can't picture yourself achieving your goal, you won't. Even Olympic athletes consult with sports psychologists to help themselves envision winning a gold medal. Your conscious and subconscious mind must know you can do it before you can win. Even if you're just beginning a fitness program or sport, you *are* an athlete. If you are new to a yoga practice, you *are* a yogini (you don't have to wait until you can do advanced poses to call yourself one). And just like strength training is necessary for increasing our muscle mass, studies are showing that concentration training, like we do in meditation, can increase brain tissue. Meditate and use positive self-talk to transcend negative thinking and motivate you toward success.

HEALTHY EATING TIPS:

- **Eat Mindfully:** Practice mindful eating. If you tend to overeat, try to eat only when you are truly hungry. If you tend to undereat and often forget to break for a meal, stop every few hours to focus on your hunger. Keep in mind that it may take practice to learn when your hunger (or lack thereof) stems from an emotional need to feel fulfilled as opposed to a physical need. Nutritionists often suggest keeping a food diary (writing down what and when you eat) to help you identify patterns of emotional eating, and to help you rethink whether you really need that snack. Knowing your triggers and being aware will help you avoid them. Use the *Healthy Eating Journal* provided at the end of this book to record daily successes and slip-ups, your feelings, and positive self-talk. During a meal, pause and become more conscious of what you are eating and you will be less likely to consume food that is bad for you and more apt to crave food that is good for you. Let all your senses – not just your taste buds – become involved. Think twice before each bite to see, smell, and feel the texture of your food. Chew slowly, and you will eat less because your brain has time to acknowledge what you are taking in, allowing you to feel satiated sooner.

- **Presentation Pleasure:** Spa chefs know that if food is presented well, a small meal will satiate even the hungriest or pickiest spa guest. Make every meal a ritual, a way of honoring your body by fueling it with healthy nutrients. Set an attractive table with flowers, coordinating napkins and placemats, and light a candle, even if you are dining alone. Create a colorful small plate that is appealing to the eye: Coordinate the color of the plate with the foods you choose, and use garnishes such as edible flowers (sweet peas and pansies in spring, chive blossoms, nasturtiums, and marigold petals in summer and fall) or fruit (sliced citrus, star fruit, and/or a few berries in winter).

- **Clean Plate Club – *Not:*** Forget what your mother said. Always leave something (just a bite) on your plate. In some countries (like Japan), a clean plate can insult a host because it sends a message that the serving was too small, and could prompt them to put more on your plate. Stay mindful and leave a bite or two on your plate to remind yourself you don't need more. This will strengthen your consciousness of what you do habitually and build discipline.

Mindfulness Tips:

- **Cultivate Awareness:** Mirrors aren't generally used during yoga or T'ai Chi practice because it is more important to notice how a posture feels on the *inside,* rather than how it looks on the outside. Self-reflection will help you to tune into your habitual tendencies. For example, try to stay aware of your spine in the cat/cow pose: You may notice that your upper back is stiff and your lower back is more flexible. If you move mindfully, you will slow down and create more mobility in your tight areas, and allow release of tension. In the same way you developed "seeing" muscles (by noticing more in nature), you can develop your "feeling" muscles (your kinesthetic sense). In yoga, the goal is not only to achieve the perfect alignment in asanas (postures), but to increase your ability to *feel* more. To feel is to bathe in the bliss of the body, accepting where you are, and it is the way to transcend judgment and criticism of yourself when you aren't able to perform perfect poses.

- **Mirror-Mirror:** If you purposely avoid mirrors, perhaps it is time to face the facts and see yourself as the world does. If you are in denial that you have gained weight, your reflection could be just the wake-up call you need. Mirrors provide truth, but they can also be used to practice compassionate self-reflection: What part of your body is the strongest, do you like the best, or are most comfortable with? What part are you most self-conscious about? Gaze at your reflection in the mirror and find all the good. Consider your family genetics and how you looked when you were younger to determine what might be *your* best potential for your current age. Accept the parts of your body you cannot change and send gratitude to them for all they do for you. When exercising, mirrors can be helpful for checking form and alignment, but in a group setting, resist comparing yourself to others.

- **Belief Journal:** Don't assume today you are the same person you were yesterday. We often distort and confuse the reality of who we are with who we once were, or who we think we should be. From time to time it's healthy to question life-long beliefs. In your journal, create two columns. In the left column, list your self-beliefs, and in the right column, whether they came from you, or someone else, and whether they still hold true. Maybe you still think of yourself as a "klutz," because that's what everyone told you when you were young, even though now you are an accomplished golfer. Or perhaps you still see yourself as a "chubby girl" because your mother always said you were even though today you wear a size 8. Or perhaps you've changed your spiritual, ethical, or worldview beliefs, assumptions, or stereotypes. Many times after paying close attention to our subconscious thoughts, we discover that our beliefs are out-dated: It's the same tape that's been playing all our lives, and it may in fact be someone else's voice we've been listening to, not even our own. How might such outdated thoughts be limiting you now? What would happen if you let one go? Your past (or your physical limitations) do not define who you are, so avoid labeling yourself if you've had a difficult time in your life, or experienced an illness or injury. Written **self-reflections** release our minds of old ways of thinking, clearing the way to **transcendence**, so we can march forward on a healthier path.

JOURNAL

Journal

April

APRIL
Spring Clean Awareness

"If we could see the miracle of a single flower clearly, our whole life would change." Buddha

April starts the season of rebirth in nature. The animal kingdom comes out of hibernation, some with their young, while other species mate and the tree and plant kingdom begin a new cycle of growth. As the earth comes alive this month, so can we. The increased light helps us shake off the lethargy of winter and move to a new rhythm. It's the ideal time to make a fresh start, reassess where we are today, and remember where we were last year, or when our wellness quest first began. Two concepts that keep us moving forward toward lasting intentions are maintaining awareness (which helps us learn to trust our instincts) and taking personal responsibility. These are two things animals do well 24/7 in order to survive in nature.

In today's modern world of asphalt jungles, it becomes harder and harder to feel, let alone trust, our instincts. To counteract that (even if you live in an urban environment) look to and be part of nature as often as possible. Observe fledglings learning to trust their instincts as they attempt to fly, while their mothers take responsibility to find food for themselves and their offspring. Delight in the first green shoots of a crocus pushing up through the earth, the fresh scent of spring air, or a leaf bud blossoming on a tree. With this fresh awareness, and with time, you will begin to notice the less obvious works of nature, and begin to see the beauty in the less perfect. Nature is perfectly *im*perfect, and so are we.

Keeping in sync with nature's cycle will help you appreciate and notice more, not only the world around you, but your own emotions and thoughts. As you notice how the sunlight at different times of the day affects the color and mood of the landscape, you will see more subtle shifts in your own temperament, and begin to observe, rather than react to, your emotions. When you are fully aware, you can stop habitual behavior or reactions. Rather than do what you've always done, you can maintain a beginner's mind: One that's thirsty to learn, tries hard, and stays positive.

Many of us are busy multi-taskers and so out of touch with our feelings that we don't know when we are out of balance. Being aware of your body and feelings will help you learn to avoid being knocked off balance. A body that is in balance craves that which keeps it there, and a body that is out of balance craves that which tilts it further away. Think of those times when you felt at the top of your game, motivated, centered, and determined not to let anything get in the way of your intentions. Now remember those other times when you were on a feeding frenzy, couldn't control sugar cravings, and kept putting exercise off for another day. Getting adequate sleep, slowing down, being in nature, and taking time for meditative practice, will help you stay in balance and be aware, so you will be able to recognize the warning signals your body sends before being thrown off balance: feeling scattered, unfocused, and pulled in different directions, which cause the balance pendulum to swing. By being mindful of your own signals, you can ground yourself with conscious breathing, solitude, and relaxation, and prevent a full upheaval. And you can learn to break away from your old "all-or-nothing" philosophy that threatens your good intentions.

The month of April is when many of us spring clean our home and property. And just as gardens need to be raked and aerated after a long season of hibernation, our skin could benefit from a thorough cleaning as well, to slough off the dead cells of winter. Treat yourself to a post-winter facial or body scrub. When our pores are thoroughly opened and cleansed, it reminds us to be more open-minded, allowing new thoughts to come in. In addition to skin treatments, a relaxing massage helps us to stay focused and in balance. Massage releases and invigorates our muscles as it energizes our minds, but its benefits are more than skin deep. Researchers who studied volunteers who received Swedish massages found the subjects had decreased blood levels of the stress hormone cortisol. Cortisol levels rise when we are stressed, and when we continue to worry, they remain high. Elevated cortisol levels not only stimulate appetite, they cause excess calories to be converted to fat deposits around the abdomen (the unhealthiest place to carry fat), which in turn can lead to Metabolic Syndrome (a precursor to adult-onset diabetes) and heart disease. If your life feels like an ongoing "stress rehearsal," schedule weekly or monthly massages to help you manage stress and your weight.

Take time in April to **spring clean** your body, home, and garden, and to connect with nature. Wakeup each morning, savor the birth of a new day, and observe the rhythm of your life in a fresh, more balanced way. Plant seeds of new hopes and intentions in the ground of your body that you wish to sow tomorrow, and renew the promises you've made for yourself. Full **awareness** of intentions that you plant today will allow you to move into the next cycle of your growth.

FITNESS TIPS:

- **Just Breathe:** Walk outdoors and take a slow, deep whiff of the sweet spring air. Feel the calmness that comes into your mind with just that one relaxing breath. Stress can cause you to take shallow sips of air, which when done habitually, can result in eventual weakness of those important intercostal muscles between the ribs that help you take deep breaths. Inhale only through your nostrils whenever possible, and find a smooth natural breath rhythm that feels right. With practice, you will be able to deepen your breaths, allowing the lung's lower lobes (the most efficient, but underutilized part) to be strengthened. Yoga and meditation practice encourage you to lengthen your breath, and through continual focus you will stay present and centered. When strength training, you are taught to exhale when lifting weights and to inhale when lowering them, to prevent elevation of blood pressure. Breath awareness is of equal importance during cardiovascular exercise when the body's demand for oxygen is so high. Learning to lengthen each breath will improve lung efficiency and help you relax and stay centered: both key essentials for improved performance.

- **Flexible Body/Flexible Mind:** Moving and stretching with more awareness will improve flexibility of mind, as well as body. A balanced yoga session flexes the spine in every direction it was made to move, while increasing the mobility and stability of all other joints and muscles. Think of stretching as spring cleansing of the body, mind, and soul; as the body opens and chakras (energy pathways) are balanced, new thoughts can be birthed. Like yoga, T'ai Chi combines meditation with slow, gentle, graceful movements that also provide many health benefits beyond enhanced flexibility of muscles and joints. If yoga or T'ai Chi is not for you, have a trainer show you some daily stretches specific to your needs. If your muscles are tight, you need to stretch daily. If you are very flexible, you may not need to stretch much at all. However, most of us have at least a few places in our body that are tight. Stretch when your muscles are warm and more pliable for maximum benefits, and to prevent injury.

- **Re-Assess and Refine:** If you are just beginning a wellness program, take time now to write down your intentions, along with your exercise plan of action. Putting it on paper and seeing it in black and white will increase the likelihood of success. Ask yourself these questions if you have been following a fitness plan for a long time, or even for a few months: Are you lifting heavier weights and/or walking/running farther? Have you lost pounds/inches/body fat since you began? Can you execute more advanced levels of Pilates/core exercises or perform previously challenging yoga poses with ease now? Use the *Activity Logs* in the back of this book to record any and all positive benefits you notice, including how you feel, your energy levels, and if you are sleeping better. Consider that it may be time to refine your exercise form with a trainer or teacher, increase your intensity, and/or upgrade your program. Maintain your motivation by trying new types of sports, classes, or instructors. Ask your teacher if you're ready to move up from the beginner yoga class to a more advanced level or style. Sign up for a 10K run to motivate you to train harder, or just to keep you running. Avoid staleness so you can maintain a beginner's mind of fresh enthusiasm, which will spur new growth and keep you in balance as you continue to spring forward.

Healthy Eating Tips:

- **"Friend" a Fat:** Healthy fats can be your friends, but do watch portion size, as they contain twice the calories (9) per gram as carbs and protein. If you already avoid unhealthy saturated fats, like butter or bacon, be sure to include healthy unsaturated fats, such as olive, grape seed, or safflower oil, or (a handful) of nuts in your diet. Nutritionists recommend a total fat consumption of 25 to 30% of daily caloric intake (or roughly 44 to 78 grams, based on a 2,000-calorie-a-day diet) for most adults. Include avocados or walnuts, which are rich in inflammation-fighting omega-3 fatty acids, but keep a healthy perspective on portions (a 1/4 cup walnuts has 18 grams fat and 190 calories, and one-half of an avocado has 15 grams fat and 165 calories). Healthy fats are important, and should not be eliminated. They transport nutrients to cells and keep blood vessels in shape, in addition to helping you feel satiated, which prevents overeating. And without a bit of oil on your green salad, you won't extract the full benefits of the nutrients.

- **Set Small Goals:** If you have a lot of weight to lose, tackle only 10 pounds at a time. If you are close to your goal (within 10 pounds), focus on the intention of losing just one pound at a time. This will make your goal feel less daunting, and the journey will be a stretch, not a strain.

- **Watch Your Whites:** Watch your intake of all white food, *except* white vegetables, like cauliflower, jicama, and fennel. Simple sugars and refined carbs, like white flour, sugar, corn syrup, pasta, and rice, contain little to no fiber or nutritional value and are just empty calories. Consuming a lot of these white foods contributes to increased fat around the middle and an elevated risk of diabetes. Switch to brown or wild rice, whole grain, or spelt pasta. Try black rice, which is high in antioxidants, fiber, and iron. Decrease your use of artificial sweeteners; because they can be 600 times sweeter than sugar, they can activate the appetite centers of the brain and cause you to crave even more food and sugar. If you can't let go of all your white foods, try to limit them to one serving per day (and eventually, one per week).

MINDFULNESS TIPS:

- **Spring Clean Your Body:** Reward yourself for having stuck with your healthy eating and exercise regime throughout the winter. Schedule a week, a few days, or just an afternoon at a spa to cleanse your body and de-stress your mind with a soothing facial, body scrub, massage, and/or a detoxifying herbal wrap. If going for just one treatment, arrive early so you have time to unwind with a cup of herbal tea, a hot tub, steam bath, or sauna: This will help you relax and enjoy your treatment even more.

- **De-Clutter:** De-clutter your mind and increase your awareness. It may be our natural instincts to tidy our nests, but being more organized does help us collect our thoughts and be more motivated to make a fresh start. Organize a junk drawer, clean a closet, or finish a long-overdue project. Use it or lose it: Donate clothes and household items you haven't used for the past year. A spacious nest helps create a spacious mind.

- **Hope Journal:** Rites of spring bring fresh inspiration for our own rebirth. What cycle of growth would you like to manifest in yourself? Are you living the life you want? Compose a timeline or a vision board of your wellness intentions or career/project hopes for the future, describing where you'd like to be in 6 months, a year, even in the next decade. (If you did this in January, it's a good time to review what you wrote and check your progress.) Trust and believe that you have the ability to achieve your new intentions just as you have fulfilled other goals in the past. Draft a fun and inspiring press release of yourself having already achieved a future goal, to help make it seem real and attainable. Explore your dharma (your soul's purpose or mission) by answering these questions in your journal: Why am I here? If I had unlimited time, energy, and money, what would I do with my life? What's stopping me from doing it now? Only when we look inside can we learn how we'd like to live outside. Create a collage of your "inside story" using images, color, and/or drawings depicting your passions and dreams. Write about the strength you receive from hope in your life, and how your **spring clean** awareness inspires you and renews your faith and trust in nature and in your own instincts.

Journal

JOURNAL

May

MAY
Nurture Respect

"We can do no great things—only small things with great love."

MOTHER TERESA

In May, as we honor our deceased on Memorial Day and our mothers on Mother's Day, why not also honor Mother Earth? Although Earth Day falls in April, the observances in May bring to mind respect, and along with that, respect for the earth. If you haven't already, it's time to go green; to reduce, reuse, recycle to help save our precious earth. Reduce your household consumption of natural resources; reuse and repurpose household items in new ways; buy sustainable products; and recycle more than you do already. You may be wondering what respecting the earth has to do with personal wellness and fitness. Through the process of showing respect for traditions and nature, we learn to respect our bodies more, and our need for exercise and healthy, natural food. As we connect more with nature, we are reminded *we are nature*. Besides the obvious benefits the earth provides – fresh air to breathe, clean water to drink, and edible food to eat – the patterns and cycles of nature teach us to accept the ebb and flow of our own growth. After all she gives to us we must **respect** Mother Earth and give back to her by doing our part to help **nurture** the world we live in.

This month, remember your mother's love and the qualities she gave you that were most nurturing to your spirit. Recall her loving care, tender touch, and ability to understand, listen, and diffuse all your worries. If you are a mother, reflect on all you do/have done to nurture your children (or pets). The love a mother gives comes from devotional respect; she respects her baby/child/teen for the individual he is and for whatever life stage he's in, and loves him unconditionally. What do you do to mother and nurture yourself? Lack of nurturing in our lives can cause us to work too much, or be too self-controlling or self-sacrificing. These behaviors leave us feeling empty and vulnerable to overconsumption of food, alcohol, or spending. Addictions to these destructive pleasures can be a way of rewarding ourselves, but they bring only momentary happiness. True joy can only be experienced when we feel whole and balanced. Having a better quality of life and nurturing relationships will restore your balance. Seek friends or family who truly listen and care about your concerns and interests – like good mothers do. And do be compassionate to others: Comfort someone who is depressed or sick, be there to listen, to give a hug, or hold a hand. When we give to others we get back what we give, but we still need to make time for our own self-care, for pleasurable pursuits, and for people whose company we fully enjoy. As women, we are born with the natural instinct to give and nurture, but we also need to receive it ourselves. Living your life this way will nurture your body, mind, and spirit.

In these modern times, Memorial Day has become for many just another holiday, a time when friends get together for a picnic or barbeque. As more people live far away from their hometowns and more people are cremated, there is less emphasis on visiting the deceased in cemeteries as there was in the past. But we can keep this important rite of respecting the dead alive by taking time to honor our departed loved ones this month. Show your patriotism by attending a ceremony or parade for the soldiers who have given their lives for our country. Placing a flower pot and saying a prayer at the graveside are old rituals, but you could create a new ritual of respect for deceased family or friends. Light a special candle and recall favorite memories, look at old photographs, or prepare a traditional dish they enjoyed. Honoring the dead may also remind you of your own mortality, and help you to let go of petty worries and be more mindful of what is truly important in your life. Make time for those you love, activities you enjoy, and for exercise.

In May, after their beds are raked and the soil is turned over, our sleeping perennial gardens awaken, renewed from the long winter and ready for their next cycle of growth. If you have been maintaining balance all winter, you too can feel this rejuvenation and be ready for more progress. In the past month, as spring began, you may have planted new seeds of awareness of your intentions, but you must continue to water and nourish those seeds. Our outside life often gets in the way of the nurturing needs of our inside life – our soul garden. Weed out things you try that don't work, and feed those that do, so that your intentions may flourish through the strength of repetition. Be outdoors whenever you can, to connect with Mother Earth. Notice the daily progress of budding plants and flowers, and envision them as your intentions taking root and blossoming, enhancing your life with the beauty of possibility.

As we find ways to respect our mothers, our departed, and Mother Earth, our self-respect blooms. Nurture this quality in yourself, and observe how your respect for others also grows. Be mindful, and you will discover small ways to nurture respect. Show respect for your home and possessions and for others' things. Respect the door (don't slam it), respect your clothes (don't throw them on the chair, hang them up), and show respect for your home and body by keeping it neat and clean. Remember that self-denial is a form of disrespect of self. Help others often by respecting what the other person needs, but take time for your own needs. Treat yourself with the same compassion and **respect** you have for others. Acknowledge all your efforts, and forgive yourself for any slip-ups. No child – even our own – is ever perfect, but we love them anyway. A flower may not be the perfect bloom, but it is still beautiful. Embrace imperfect beauty in yourself. Plant and **nurture** your own garden instead of waiting for someone else to bring you flowers.

Fitness Tips:

- **Earth Energy**: Walk or run outdoors as many days as you can to reconnect to the earth and be recharged. With each step you take, focus on the kinesthetic awareness of your feet contacting the ground, and how the earth supports you as you absorb her energy. Repeat simple positive affirmations to yourself (one syllable per step) and visualize the message being imprinted into every cell in your body with each foot strike. Look straight ahead and to your right and left to see what is ahead. Use your eyes to look down to avoid potholes or obstacles in your path, rather than dropping your head. With the head upright, good posture and more efficient breathing can be maintained. Relax the shoulders and let your arms swing to help you balance and move more freely. Focus on the sights, sounds, and smells of spring: The morning dew on the vernal green grass, the bird song of a robin, the pungent smell of the lilacs. With each step, imagine moving forward on your life path and respect and be grateful for the energy the earth gives back to you.

- **Core Care:** The core muscles are the smallest muscles of the body that innervate the spine, pelvis, and scapulae. They allow us to maintain good posture, balance, and stability, and strengthening them will also help avoid back pain or injury. Consult a fitness trainer or a Pilates instructor for a personalized core training program if you have a history of disc or spinal injuries or surgeries. Respect your core and try these two simple, but effective exercises three times per week:

  1. **Plank:** Lying face down with legs straight, prop yourself up on your forearms, with elbows directly below the shoulders. Curl your toes under and lift body to parallel position so only forearms and toes are in contact with floor. (If this is too difficult, drop knees to floor.) Maintain a neutral spine (the natural curve), breathe, and hold for 10 seconds or more. Build up to 1 to 2 minutes.

  2. **Bridge:** Lie on back with knees bent, feet hip-width apart directly below knees, and arms by your sides. Lift torso up off floor, maintaining a neutral spine. (Keep head, shoulders, and feet on floor.) Lift and lower slowly 10 times, pausing after the lift.

- **Nurture Changes:** Nature doesn't hurry, so why should we? The seasons change gradually, so respect your own need for gradual changes, too. If you hate exercise or have trouble altering an unhealthy habit, shrink the change. Small changes are more likely to be absorbed. Make a commitment to exercise or change just one day per week. When the new habit becomes easier, add another day to your schedule, and when ready, a third day. Eventually, you will find yourself choosing to follow healthy habits the majority of days, because you feel better when you do. Stay aware, and focus on the benefits of your new rituals. Remember that if changes are too drastic, you won't stick with them.

HEALTHY EATING TIPS:

- **Go Green:** Eat five servings (1/2 cup ea. = 2 ½ cups total) of fruit and veggies daily, and include at least one leafy green, along with as many other bright colors as possible. Darker-colored produce (like spinach, red peppers, blueberries, yams, and oranges) provide important vitamins and minerals and support the immune system. If weight loss or maintenance is your goal, order a small green salad and a soup *or* appetizer in lieu of a main entrée when dining out. When dining in, one day a week have soup and salad as your main meal. As often as possible, eat locally grown organic food. Respect the earth and your body, but anticipate exceptions to your diet and go with the flow. You'll be a happier person for it, especially if you're respectful of people who invite you to dinner or offer to cook for you.

- **Conquer Cravings:** Manage stress (using deep breaths, meditation, and/or exercise), move daily, get enough sleep, and keep blood sugar levels balanced by eating four to five *small* healthy meals throughout day to help conquer cravings. But don't deny yourself the occasional treat; *sometimes* it's best to nurture your craving and have a small portion of what you really want. You can overeat when you can't satisfy a craving, continually trying different foods and consuming more calories in the end. So go ahead and enjoy a 1-ounce piece of 60% cacao dark chocolate guilt-free. The flavanoids it contains act like antioxidants, which help lower bad (LDL) cholesterol and blood pressure.

- **Become a Flexitarian:** Hate the thought of giving up barbequed chicken or the occasional In-N-Out burger? Eat a vegetarian diet most of the time, and dabble in turkey or fish some of the time. Think pro-plant, not anti-meat lifestyle. And if you do eat red meat, choose to graze on lean cuts of grass-fed beef, which contains two to three times more heart-healthy omega-3s than corn-fed beef. If you currently have a meat-heavy diet, start slowly with meatless Mondays, and eventually progress to 2 days per week. Your meat cravings should subside as you get used to eating less, and you may be able to advance to 3 to 5 meatless days per week. Or become a "social carnivore" and cook only plant-based food at home, and save meat for special outings and social events.

MINDFULNESS TIPS:

- **Get Grounded:** During yoga standing poses, imagine yourself as a tree: your feet as the roots, your legs the trunk, and your arms the branches. Feel the stability and balance, as well as the centering and calmness that come with that grounding practice. Think of how many years it takes for trees to grow tall, and how the roots are laid down first, but continue to support and stabilize, even with the increased height. Observe a tree swaying in heavy winds, anchored by its strong roots. Be rooted to your intentions with that same tenacity. In corpse pose, as you lie flat, feel how the earth supports you. When walking outdoors, as you breathe in, visualize oxygen coming into your lungs, and as you breathe out, visualize carbon dioxide being released from your body. Observe the green world that surrounds you (the trees, grass, and vines) and remember that they breathe in carbon dioxide and in turn, release oxygen back to the environment. Feel that interconnectedness – your lungs and the green world – keeping each other alive. We are nature. Nothing is separate.

- **Small Acts of Kindness:** Think of a small act of kindness you could do to brighten someone's day. Re-enact the old May Day tradition: Leave an anonymous bouquet or basket of fresh flowers on someone's door step. When we give without thought as to what we might get back in return, we gain happiness and contentment. Give yourself a gift of nurturing touch, like a massage or manicure. Beside the obvious benefits, touching activates body receptors that release oxytocin, a hormone known for its positive effects on well-being and relaxation.

- **Soul Journal:** Honor a deceased loved one by journaling about a favorite memory or write her a letter to help soothe your grief. Think about the ways you show respect to yourself and the respect you give to others, and how it makes you feel. Journal

about that respect or from nature, or the Despite success in areas, do you still feel you need to make you forever seek to evolve check-in on our soul's about the peace you receive bliss you feel when gardening. your career, family, or other unfulfilled? Write about what feel whole. Our spirit and soul and grow, so it's important to needs from time to time. By journaling, you can study the text of your life, gain insight into the nature of your intentions, and find ways to show **respect** that will **nurture** the garden of your soul.

MAY

Journal

Journal

June

JUNE
Lighten Up

"We do not stop playing because we grow old; we grow old because we stop playing." MARCEL PROUST

With the arrival of June and more hours of daylight, we too can **lighten up**. School's out, the carefree days of summer are here, and so is the natural urge to be less rigid. This concept of easing up was ingrained in us in our youth, which can make it difficult to continue our normal regimens, especially if we have children home for the summer. Don't fight the urge: Go with the flow of the season, and break away from your usual routine. Add some fun and adventure to your longer days. It doesn't mean you have to take up a high-risk pursuit like hang-gliding; just go beyond your comfort zone and try a new sport or class. If you're a Northerner, it's time to take it outside. Join a boot camp class at the beach or park, swim, play tennis, ride your bike, or plan weekly walks with friends. If you're a Southerner, it might be necessary to take it inside, or exercise earlier or later than usual outdoors to avoid the heat. Get up early to witness the first light of the day and experience inner stillness. Practice morning yoga sun salutations outdoors to awaken the body, focus the mind, and express reverence for being alive. Take some deep breaths. Visualize the sun inside your heart and feel the warmth in yourself.

If you are someone who never varies your schedule, plan a summer vacation to avoid burnout. Get away if you can, to savor nature's simple pleasures at the beach, lake, or mountains. A change of scenery makes it easier to change up a routine and relax. The most rejuvenating vacation is one that allows you to do the opposite of what you normally do. If your job requires you to do a lot of speaking or socializing, choose a quiet retreat. If your constant and sole companion is your desk, laptop or iPhone, seek social getaways, like an organized group trip to trek or cycle, or go to a spa. If you sit for hours in your office, go for a swim, sail, walk, or hike. If you hit the gym hard every day, or if your work is physical or keeps you on your feet, participate in more playful outdoor activities and relax on the beach to catch up on that novel you started months ago.

If you can't get away, try, as an experiment – just for a week – to slow down, work less, and refrain from excess stimulus and over-exercising. Be more mindful of what you do and say habitually. As we tend to justify our formed habits, our mind tries to convince ourselves we are right. Being too rigid can also affect your thinking. If you've already made a lot of progress this year, consider the idea of simply maintaining your weight or present fitness level this month or this season. Give yourself the leisure of coasting, instead of pushing ahead. When you do resume your normal routine, it will feel fresh and new again. Do continue to have a healthy eating plan to avoid weight gain; just allow yourself the occasional treat so you won't feel deprived. (When everyone else is eating an ice cream cone, you can order a small non-fat frozen yogurt for yourself.) Coasting this way for awhile will keep your weight at a plateau if you stay mindful, and when fall comes it will be easier to go back to fewer calories and to lose weight. Embrace challenge and change; shift perception and be more flexible in your thinking. Adventure has an unknown outcome – like life itself.

In June, when the sun is the strongest in the northern hemisphere, soak up its extra radiance and warmth. Although sunscreen can protect the skin from harmful ultraviolet rays, it can negatively affect the body's ability to produce vitamin D. Research has long shown that vitamin D plays an important role in the absorption of calcium into the bones, but more recent studies suggest the vitamin may also reduce the risk of heart attack, stroke, and certain cancers, and that higher doses may positively affect depression and autoimmune diseases. To ensure adequate vitamin D levels, some doctors suggest forgoing sunscreen on the limbs as you soak up 10 to 15 minutes a day of sunshine. The rest of the time, wear a 30SPF broad-spectrum sunscreen and a hat to prevent sun overexposure, which can cause cancer and early aging of the skin. Vitamin D occurs naturally in salmon, liver, and egg yolks, but many foods, such as dairy products, cereals, and breads are fortified with it. If you are over 40 your body has more difficulty absorbing vitamin D from the sun, and if you don't get 10 to 15 minutes of daily sunshine you could also be deficient. A simple blood test can confirm if you are deficient. As of 2012, the daily amount needed is under review, so some health care professionals are recommending much higher amounts than the formally suggested supplementation of 600 International Units (IU).

On the darkest days, when you or the world is in turmoil, the sun may still shine its rays on the earth, spreading hope. Remember that the sun inevitably comes out following Mother Nature's most destructive storms. Can you still shine when all your efforts don't produce the results you anticipated? It actually is possible to feel happy even when you're not as successful as you thought you'd be, or when friends or family let you down, or when the state of the world is unsettling. Seek solace in nature to help you detach from negative feelings and help you find the simple joys that will bring light to even your darkest days. Slow down and do less multi-tasking, so you can savor what you are doing in the present. Find your sense of humor and use positive thoughts to counter negative ones. And smile more. Not little phony smiles, but big genuine smiles. Studies have shown that people who smile more are indeed happier, have more stable relationships, develop better interpersonal skills, and live 7 years longer. So, be the happiness guru. Look for traits you admire in people and compliment them, thank people for all they do for you, and be grateful for all you have and all you are.

This month, honor the summer solstice and **lighten up**. Add some adventure and fun, soak up the sun, smile, and bask in the glow of your healthy radiance and positive attitude.

Fitness Tips:

- *Go Barefoot:* Let your feet breathe outside the confinement of shoes for a few hours a day if possible. If you have tender feet or worry about uncleanly walking surfaces, try "barefoot shoes" (thin-soled shoes with no cushioning), which make you *feel* shoeless, increasing your kinesthetic awareness of the earth beneath your feet. Feet get lazy from wearing athletic shoes that support the arches, and even more so if you wear orthotics. One of the benefits of yoga (due to being barefoot) is increased circulation in the feet, and strengthening of the arches and foot muscles. Try "barefoot running shoes" which tout a closer connection to the environment and a more natural movement that strengthens the feet and leg muscles. (However, they are not advisable for anyone with foot problems or orthopedic concerns where cushioning and stability in a shoe is essential.) Running form must be changed from heel striking to mid-foot striking first (as you would naturally run without shoes), with foot strike beneath hips rather than extended far from the body. Consult a trainer or running coach for help with proper gait and form. *Progress slowly from regular running shoes to going barefoot.* Condition the feet by doing indoor activities barefoot, or walking on sand or grass for a couple weeks before progressing to running. Start with short barefoot runs 3 times per week, increasing duration each week, and wait 4 weeks before adding more barefoot run days. And if you run on the street or sidewalks, it's best to wear the barefoot running shoes to protect your feet from glass, pebbles, and burns from hot pavement.

- **Join the *Green* Gym:** In Japan, exercising in nature is called *shinrin-yoku* (forest-air bathing), and in the UK, people exercising in forested areas refer to it as the "green gym." Studies show that as little as 5 minutes of exercise in nature boosts self-esteem, lowers stress, decreases depression, and increases liveliness. If you belong to a gym, inquire about their "freeze" policy. Most fitness clubs allow you to take up to 3 months off with no monthly fee if you write a letter of request ahead of time. Take to the trails or streets for your walks or runs, or to a lake or ocean for your swims. Take rubber tubing outside for an alfresco variation from indoor machines or free weights. (Tubing also fits easily in your travel bag; so you can take your strength training on the road to your summer get-away.) Your muscles don't know the difference between dumbbells or tubing. As long as the resistance is challenging, they will become stronger.

- **Active Recovery Workouts:** More playful or recreational workouts are a vital part of an injury-free and balanced weekly workout plan. For bodies over 40 in particular, recovery (easier) cardio days are needed in between high-intensity workouts, for both muscle repair and for the replenishment of energy stores. These "active rest" days can actually help prevent muscle soreness more than just plain rest. Plan at least one low-intensity cardio workout per week, or choose this month to lighten up all your sessions, opting instead for longer, easier exercise outdoors. Swimming, biking, surfing, paddle-boarding, tennis, or golfing (if you walk the course) are lighter warm-weather alternatives. By doubling your normal exercise time, the calorie burn should be about the same as a shorter, harder workout. For those who do a lot of active gardening, 4 hours would be the calorie equivalent of an average one hour gym session. These easier workouts also give you the added bonus of increasing the size and number of muscle mitochondria (the fat-burning "stoves" in your body).

HEALTHY EATING TIPS:

- **Water Wisely:** Most healthy adults should drink about eight 8-ounce glasses of fluids a day. But in summer, when exercising in heat, or during long endurance bouts over an hour, you need at least 16 ounces more, for a total intake of 80-ounces per day. (Be cautious, however, as over-watering can be as dangerous to your health as under-watering.) Almost all liquids can count, but to avoid weight gain, skip juices and sodas, which are high in sugar and calories. Contrary to dated beliefs, new studies have discovered that caffeinated beverages do *not* zap the body's water reserves, so unsweetened tea and coffee can count. Hydrate 20 minutes before you begin your workout to allow the water to be absorbed into your cells and muscles, and then drink during and after, especially if you perspire a lot. Any temperature beverage is fine, but in hot weather, cold water can help cool the body down. Headache, sore joints, rapid pulse, light-headedness, and fatigue can be signs of dehydration. Even slight dehydration can put a strain on the heart, impair concentration, and slow metabolism, so stay healthily hydrated.

- **Pleasure Principle:** Follow a healthy diet most of the time, but allow yourself the occasional indulgence. Plan a favorite *small* treat once per week, if weight loss is your goal, or once per day if it's not. Its okay: You *can* have a healthy relationship with food if you lighten up and learn to enjoy those small treats without guilt. If you aim for perfection 100% of the time you're more apt to binge and you're probably not enjoying the pleasures of life. When out to dinner with a group of friends or family, order one dessert for the whole table. Take one bite and pass it around. The first bite is the one that tastes the best, anyway. Savor it, and enjoy.

- **Snack Smart:** Skip the chips and salsa, and instead make popcorn for your next cookout, beach party or ball park adventure. Air pop or stove top with a little canola oil, but skip the high-fat/preservatives in microwave popcorn packs. Or recreate a childhood pleasure: Buy an old-fashioned popcorn popper and cook it over the campfire. Toss with pepper, parmesan cheese, chili powder, or a small amount of sea salt. Popcorn is technically a whole grain, so it's high in fiber and low in calories, and each shiny kernel holds a potent dose of healthy antioxidants.

MINDFULNESS TIPS:

- **Be a Kid:** Be silly, giggle, have fun. Build a sandcastle or bury yourself in sand at the beach. Run through a sprinkler, climb on the monkey bars, balance walk on a curb, ride your bike through a mud puddle: get wet, laugh, and shout with ecstasy. With a child's mind, take a leap into the unknown and feel the power of pure recharged joy. And rediscover the simplicity and art of relaxation by doing nothing. Lie in a hammock or on the grass under a tree, and gaze at the leaves and the sky above. Take a deep breath. Notice the sweet smell of fresh mown grass. Listen for the buzzing of bees or the distant drone of a lawn mower – such a comforting sign of summer in the North after a long cold winter. Feel the warm air or sun on your skin. Tune in to your pets' world and bask in their unconditional love and happiness. Play card or board games with family or friends. Toss a ball or Frisbee with a young child; you'll both release the "happy" hormone oxytocin, which lowers blood pressure and cortisol.

- **Go With the Flow:** Fifteen minutes of yoga daily is the equivalent of one full class per week, but with the added benefit of a more frequent spiritual connection. If classes don't fit into your summer schedule, try yoga on your own at home, outdoors, or with a DVD or a podcast. Keep your mind open and receptive to trying new teachers and different styles of yoga. Practice being flexible in your mind as you work on being more flexible in your body, so when a favorite teacher moves away, or the schedule changes, you can go with the flow and stay with your practice.

- **Joy Journal:** In honor of Father's Day, write about a special experience you had with your dad or the qualities you admire in him. What traits of his do you have? Send a letter to someone telling them how much you appreciate them. Or journal about what makes you happy, a favorite childhood memory of a carefree summer day, or compose a list of fun things you want to do this summer. Try using crayons or bright-colored magic markers to enliven the page and bring out the fun factor. Printing with crayons can help take you back to how you felt as a child. Decorate your pages with glitter, stickers, and drawings. When you have a blissful experience, write about it. Studies have found that journaling about simple joys in your life, or what you are grateful for, increases the happiness factor and deepens the experience. As you spend more time outdoors absorbing the sunlight this month, let the sun shine within you – and **lighten up.**

Journal

Journal

July

JULY
Celebrate Your Independence

"Life begins on the edge of your comfort zone."

July – as the United States celebrates Independence Day – is an opportune time to **celebrate** the freedom of choice we have to live our lives in a healthy and balanced way. Our current restraints and our future liberty are our choice. This means celebrating the freedom we have to be unattached to outcomes, with the ability to find joy regardless of circumstances. Celebrating the freedom we have to change who we are, to move forward to unknown territory. **Celebrating** our freedom of **independence** from self-limiting or addictive behavior and the obstacles we place in our way on our road to fulfillment.

A big part of independence depends on our ability to accept change, and deal with unexpected or unwelcome outcomes. Drastic changes in our lives beyond our control – death, illness, or natural disasters – are the most difficult of all, because it's hard to see the good when something bad happens. But if we practice acceptance of life's minor disappointments, and learn to appreciate the simple joys of the everyday experience, it makes it easier to cope and find eventual peace during life's major upsets. Choosing to enjoy the tennis match, even when you're losing; moving on and refocusing on a new goal after being overlooked for a job promotion; or letting go of anger when it rains the day of your outdoor party are all examples of small opportunities to seek unconditional happiness. Bumps in the road that impede our progress and dark clouds along our life path will happen to most of us. But the good news is that these challenges help us to appreciate our health and good fortune when we are on a smooth road and the sun *is* shining.

Seek freedom from the fears that prevent you from fully engaging in life. Fear of changing who you are, of letting go of unhealthy habits, people, or thoughts, or fear of failure. Sometimes our fears are with us so long we forget that we do have a choice: We could learn to let them go and be independent at last. Fears are not who you are, they are a *feeling* you have. The longer you live with a fear, the smaller your world becomes and the more your comfort zone shrinks. The Kaizen principle – a Japanese philosophy that loosely translated means "baby steps" – is a simple way to make small lifestyle changes one step at a time. For example, if you have a fear of heights you could confront it by going close to the edge of your comfort zone – the point where you start to feel anxiety. Maybe it's a short walk up a little hill taking deep breaths and using positive self-talk to help you relax and acknowledge that you are okay. The next day you can expand the boundaries a little more by going up a higher hill, maybe one with a view. Each time thereafter, you will learn what your edge is, and how close you can get to it. It is at the edge of your comfort zone where the most learning can occur. Courage is the willingness to experience our fears, and as we experience our fears, courage grows. You have the freedom of choice to stay with what you know (even if you are fully aware that it's self-limiting), or free yourself and enhance your life.

Look at relationships in your life and consider whether you are attached or dependent on them for your personal happiness. Do you feel joy independent of others? If you can, and have a partner who is also whole, you can share a healthy relationship. Are you attached to your children and fearful of their independence, when they no longer need you or when they go away to school? As you grow more mindful of your own needs and fulfill your own life purpose, you will have less desire to control others. Nurture and love your children, but just like the birds, you need to trust they can fly on their own once they leave the nest. Not only will your relationships improve with the practice of non-attachment, but it will also help you stay centered when circumstances are beyond your control. Anticipate that there will be times you will revert to your old ways. If you stay mindful, you can catch yourself acting habitually and then change to more mindful behavior. The act of being aware of when we are mindless is, in fact, being mindful.

We outgrow many things, but if we are not mindful we may not be aware of when it's time to move on, or if we are afraid we may not want to change. A lobster periodically outgrows its shell – its home – that was once a perfect fit. While the larger shell is forming, it must come out and survive for several days unprotected and vulnerable to predators. If this process did not take place, the lobster would suffocate and die within the confinement of its old shell. This is a metaphor for our own evolution. If you stay too safe the spirit inside will wither and die. Take 10 to 15 minutes daily – in nature if possible – to meditate with the intention of going within and seeking what it is you need to make you feel whole, to make you shine from the inside. Don't focus on material things or other people, but on qualities you must bring to yourself or to your life. If you have been frozen in fear, afraid to fulfill your life purpose, or have yet to discover your life mission, you will not feel whole. What's missing that makes you feel empty? Are you relying on others to make you feel whole? By asking yourself questions and exploring within, in time you will eventually find what it is you need to complete yourself. Free yourself of thinking that is dependent on past beliefs and values, and let new more independent thoughts come in. Focus on the positive in your life and in yourself, and express gratitude daily. Practice unconditional happiness by finding joy in simple things you take for granted, much like a child, or animal does.

Loosen your grip. It's human nature to resist change and stay with the easy way, but we respond well to variation throughout the year. Just as we may crave a little rain after endless days of sunshine, our bodies and spirits crave something different, too. Change can be challenging, but if you learn to ride the tides of life with grace, you can take on the biggest waves and – even if you get wiped out – end up on the water's surface. **Celebrate** the changes you've made in the spirit of **independence** this month, and let your personal freedom ring true in your heart.

Fitness Tips:

- **Early Bird or Night Owl:** The optimal time to exercise is when our energy level is highest, but for many of us that time has to be whenever we can fit it into our schedules. If you don't function well in the morning, you'll have a more productive workout later in the day. With this season of extra daylight, consider early morning or after dinner outdoor exercise to beat the heat, or to experience nature at its best. The change of workout time could enliven your workout as you take advantage of the extra light. Recall the summers of your youth when you were allowed to play outside until dark and how freeing and fun that was after a winter indoors. Walk or run very early or late in the day to observe the changing light in the sky, the stars, or the moon, to help build appreciation for the earth. But avoid any high-intensity exercise after 8:00 PM, as it might affect your ability to get to sleep. If you are very flexible, exercising in the morning when your muscles are tighter and more stable can decrease the risk of injury. If you are very tight and stiff, exercising later in the day will be easier on your body and you won't have to spend as much time warming up.

- **Sedentary Strategy:** If your summers find you stuck inside, cozying up to the air conditioner, it's time to find a gym to work out in. But even if you exercise 1 hour every day, the remaining hours of the day you spend sitting increases your risk of heart disease and mortality. Prolonged sitting (4 or more hours at a time) causes a greater amount of fat to accumulate in the bloodstream and on your waistline. If you are sedentary, or your job requires you to sit, develop a strategy to move more. When possible, schedule walking meetings or get-togethers instead of lunches or coffees. Get up and move every 30 minutes; stand up and walk when you talk on the phone; use stairs instead of the elevator; and park your car the farthest away. Studies have shown that walking for just 5 minutes increases circulation, energy, and mood for up to 2 hours after. Standing instead of sitting for just 1 hour per day burns an extra 100 calories. (Standing could be broken up into four 15-minute or six 1-minute daily sessions.) Consider purchasing a stand-up desk or workstation for your office. Adding 2.5 hrs/day of movement (@350 extra calories burned) could result in an approximate annual weight loss of 36 pounds.

- **Surf & Turf It:** Prevent staleness by freeing yourself of your usual routine. If you always do land-based workouts, add some aquatic sessions, like swimming or aqua aerobics; if you're always in the water, switch to land once or twice a week. Vary your run/walk route; even going in the opposite direction will change the scenery and be a departure from your normal routine. Try changing the days or times you exercise, or the type of class, or try a different teacher. If you always choose the same place in the class, move to the opposite side of the room. Switch up the weight training exercises you do, or have a trainer design you a new program. Become more mindful and change your habitual routines, and free yourself, also, of habitual thinking.

Healthy Eating Tips:

- **Divide and Conquer:** Celebrate your freedom of independence by not giving in to a restaurant's idea of portion size, which is often more than double the amount of food you need. When you place your order, ask the server to bring a to-go box at the same time the food is served, so you can immediately place half in the box to save for a meal the next day. Eating large portions of even low-calorie foods expands the stomach, increasing the appetite for the next meal. The stomach organ is like skin: As it ages, it becomes less elastic, so if it expands on a regular basis, it might not shrink back to its original size.

- **Twenty-Minute Rule:** It takes about 20 minutes before your stomach feels full, so if you eat too fast you won't know when you've had enough, until too late. Be mindful of every bite. Take small bites, and chew slowly 5 to 10 times per bite to truly taste and enjoy your food.

- **A Glass a Day Keeps the Doctor Away?:** One glass of red wine or one shot of spirits has long been touted to prevent some diseases and be healthy for the heart. Now the most recent research warns that one glass per day can increase a woman's risk of breast cancer. If you do choose to drink alcohol, consider adopting "Wine Wednesdays" and/or "Wine Weekends" as a compromise to daily consumption.

MINDFULNESS TIPS:

- **Just Say No:** Learn to say "no" to social obligations you really don't need or want to attend. Resist replying to every text or email you receive. Choose to answer messages only when necessary, and restrain from continually feeling the need to check in. Disconnect whenever you can from the electronic world, and reconnect with your inner world. Reflect on the relationships you have. It's important to have someone to commiserate with, but be sure to balance negativity with a good dose of pleasurable conversation. Are you living your own life guided by your *own* intentions, or are you easily influenced by others? Let go of toxic friendships, or any you no longer enjoy. Notice how the extra space you create for yourself allows a new part of you to surface. Journal about it and the empowerment you feel from the freedom of choice you exercised.

- **Sociable or Solitary:** Most of us have sociable and solitary time built into our day. It's important to balance both, so if you have too much of one and not the other, look for ways to add more of what is missing. If your days are packed with constant social interaction, find time to be alone to be free from the need to be with or care for others. Practice being independent, being happy alone, listening to your own thoughts, enjoying your own company. If, on the other hand, you spend all or most of your time alone, seek some socialization. Loners can benefit from a group class or exercising in a gym, whereas social butterflies may need a solitary workout or the wide-open space of nature. Practice the spirit of independence while also enjoying the camaraderie of others. Practice freedom of choice by choosing who you'd like to spend time with.

- **Letter/List Writing Journal**: Write letters that you never send. If you didn't get to say good-bye to someone who passed away or never had the opportunity to speak your mind when a relationship ended, write a letter to that person. Even more powerful: Write a letter to yourself, from that person who is gone now, with the words you would have liked to have heard. You might be surprised at what you write. When composing a letter through someone else's mind, we remember that person, who he was and what he was capable of based on that. This sheds light on and allows us to see another's viewpoint, and understand where he was coming from. Seeing things through his eyes helps us to release anger, forgive, and move on. Address and "mail" the letter in your journal, or burn it and send it off to the Universe in an ethereal cloud of smoke. This process  will help bring closure to pain and grief, and help you move freely into your future, independent of your past. Compose a list of pros and cons (side-by-side in your journal) of the changes you'd like to make in your life. Seeing both sides (i.e., the reasons why you need to make this change and what fears are holding you back) will help validate the actions you choose to take. In the spirit of **independence**, take charge of your life, and be ready to **celebrate** change.

JOURNAL

August

AUGUST
Patience and Acceptance

"Nature does not hurry, yet everything is accomplished."

LAO-TZU

During the dog days of summer, on those sweltering high mercury days, **patience** can also melt in the heat. Perhaps we feel anxious because the summer is almost over and we haven't done half the things we wanted to. Or conversely, we're antsy from the lethargy of the season, impatient for the cool and more structured days of fall. All those feelings can cause us to become impatient for results from our fitness and nutrition efforts. Just as a mountain has plateaus along the way to the summit, we face plateaus along our wellness journey. Nature teaches us the trite but true lesson: All things take time. As you gaze at a majestic mountain range, or even rocks on a beach, imagine their beginning, as a single grain of sand, and how many billions of years it took to form stone. Whether on a hike or in life, plateaus are there to give us a place to catch our breath and to observe the view, and to see and appreciate how far we've come. And with this pause, our body can **accept** where it is and adapt to the new demands we've placed on it, and respond, in time, with growth or visible changes – just as nature intended.

Sometimes we find ourselves so fixated on perfection and future results we don't enjoy what we're doing in the present. To build patience and help you stay open to learning, practice contentment. Appreciate your small successes, the subtle changes or ease with which you perform an activity or sport that will add up and make a difference in the end. Keep your goal in mind, but avoid fixating on it. And accepting where you are doesn't mean you stop striving or become complacent, especially if you practice unhealthy lifestyle habits, or have yet to get moving.

Apply this yoga principle to all your workouts to keep you mindful and aware of when it is safe to push, and when it is not: *When we feel, we cannot force, and when we force, we cannot feel.* By feeling or paying attention to the intensity or effect an exercise or workout has on your body, you will know when it's safe to push. Alternatively, when you are not paying attention to how your body feels, you cannot be aware of or heed its signal to back off what you're doing, leading you to push too far. *Feeling* lowers blood pressure, fosters acceptance and compassion, and decreases risk of injury. *Forcing*, on the other hand, elevates blood pressure, fosters anger and aggression, and increases risk of injury. Staying mindful of how your muscles, breath, and body feel will familiarize you with your true edge – that point where the exercise gets hard – and you will learn when it's safe to push more and when it's not.

Pushing too fast takes away from the joy of the journey, and it's easy to miss things along the way or get injured. Injuries force us to re-learn those lessons the hard way. Slow down. Be patient. Accept where you are now. Take the time to heal and use it as an opportunity to improve another aspect of your body or life. If you have a lower-body injury, devote more workout time to your upper body, and vice versa. When you can't exercise at all, you have more time to focus on broadening your mind through meditation. Meditation can help ease pain by re-directing your attention to your breath. As you inhale, imagine healing energy coming into your body, and as you exhale, imagine the pain going out of your body. Reflect on how and why the injury happened, so you can avoid going down that path again.

If you exercise too much, perhaps what you have is an overuse injury. When we go beyond the boundaries of what is considered necessary for our particular life functions, health, and well-being, we are exercising our egos. Sometimes we can't stop moving and exercising because we don't want to acknowledge or face our feelings. When we are not content with who we are inside, our egos hunger for gratification. It's easy to become caught up in the mental whirlwind that presses us to be obsessed with the way we look, to desire more, or to expect results too soon. Will running a faster mile really make you happier if the training it requires infringes on the time and energy you have for your family or spouse? Does a day full of non-stop activities fulfill or deflate you? Try doing as little of the unnecessary "shoulds" as you have to, and make time for more of the things that give you energy. Are you driven by peers or long-held beliefs to desire more? Question whether the goal of running your first marathon to celebrate your 50th birthday is truly your own, or if it's what your friends have done, or what you feel you "should" do to prove you are age-resistant.

We admire young saplings for their slender, resilient trunks, but we also appreciate old trees for their gnarled, but grand trunks. So, too, should we view our own aging process. The majority of older Americans who were interviewed as part of an ongoing retrospective study reported that old age exceeded their expectations. Even those who could no longer do the physical things they used to love doing felt a sense of contentment and happiness that they had not experienced earlier in their life. Most of those studied recommended that others embrace aging, not fight it; to think of it as both an attitude and a process. Instead of feeling jealous of the beauty of a young woman, or feeling angry that your body won't let you run anymore, be grateful that you, too, were beautiful in your youth and ran many miles in your past. Enjoy your memories of the past, but live peacefully in the present by appreciating the wisdom you have gained through the years. Adapt an attitude of gratitude and acceptance for what your body *can* do, even if it means pausing on your current plateau, and eventually descending to an even lower mountain vista. Each decade brings opportunities for new horizons and outlooks. And if you *are* still young, take care of your body, mind, and spirit and live up to their full potential, so you won't grow old with regret.

Nature doesn't hurry, so regardless of what stage of life you are in, **accept** plateaus and practice **patience**. Be content, but not complacent, with where you are now. Celebrate the good in each moment and each day. Create a journey as joyful as your destination.

Fitness Tips:

- **Anticipate Speed Bumps:** In the Northeast, katydids (a relative of crickets and grasshoppers) begin to sing their mating calls near the end of August. Their chorus gets louder as the summer draws to a close, signaling that cooler weather is on its way. With the approach of fall – a busier season for many of us – you may be dreading the end of summer and its abundant time for recreation and exercise, or time with your kids. Expect *and* accept that there will be times in your life when interruptions will be out of your control. When your career forces you to travel more, or your child's sports schedule requires you to drive daily to the soccer field, or if medical conditions or injuries limit your activity, look at it as your "off-season," a time when you back-off your usual routine a little, knowing that you'll be back to your "in-season" schedule again soon. Stay positive, and be patient. Remember that there are seasons for everything, just like nature. If it's just a one-day glitch in your schedule, plan an alternative time to work out, like your lunch hour. Have dedicated days/times to exercise, and a set program to follow. If you miss a day, get back to your schedule as soon as possible. And be present so you can be on guard the next time you allow others to talk you out of your workout. You can create a new habit of saying "no" if you pay attention.

- **Patience Training:** When strength training, start with a weight you can lift comfortably while still maintaining proper form and alignment. Avoid quick or jerky movements; keep each move smooth and controlled, especially the lowering phase. Wait until good form is established, before increasing the weights. This rule also applies to yoga postures: Don't be tempted to advance a pose if you can not perform the beginner or basic version well. With practice and persistence, you'll get stronger, and your body will let you know when it is ready for the next level.

- **Two-More Reps Rule:** During strength training when it gets hard and you want to stop, say to yourself: "I can do two more reps." In cardio, use the same principle, substituting minutes for reps. In yoga, substitute breaths; when you feel like coming out of the pose, try to stay for two more deep breaths. (Remember this does *not* mean to push to unsafe levels or to sacrifice form that could cause harm.) We are conditioned to stop simply because we're impatient. Almost always we can do two more and that's how you continue to get results. Remembering this principle will also help you stay mindful and aware as you exercise.

HEALTHY EATING TIPS:

- **Protein Power:** Most women should get 6 ounces of lean protein (or about 60 to 90 grams) each day. Protein provides the amino acids essential for growth and repair of tissue, bones, and muscle. You don't need excessive amounts, but if you don't get enough, it will affect your ability to get stronger and may even increase your craving for sweets. Vegetarians need to consume a variety of plant-based proteins, such as a cup of soybeans or lentils (18g), kidney beans (13g), or quinoa (8g), throughout the day to obtain all the essential amino acids the body requires. Fish, poultry, meat, and dairy, such as 6 oz. low-fat plain Greek yogurt (18g), or two large eggs (12g), provide a source of complete (balanced amino acids) protein. Limit red meat to one serving per week, due to its higher cholesterol and fat content. (Choose lean cuts, and trim all visible fat.) If you have made attempts to go more vegetarian in the past, have patience with your taste buds and habits, and don't give up. Give fish, tofu, or grains another chance and learn new ways to prepare them. We can train our taste buds with time. Start by becoming a "two-thirds vegetarian" and eating meat at only one meal per day. By weaning yourself off meat slowly, you will crave it less.

- **Downsize Your Dishes:** Savvy spas know this secret: Studies have found that when small portions of food are served on a smaller plate, people are satisfied with less. Using salad plates for the main course will make the portion size looks larger. A tiny serving of sorbet won't look small if served in a doll-sized cup or saucer, and an espresso spoon will ensure mindful bites that sweeten the experience. If weight loss is your goal, downsize your portions *and* your dishes.

- **Emotions Eating You Up:** Have a plan of action for those vulnerable times when you might overindulge. Call a friend who always seems to sooth your nerves, and make a date to watch a favorite comedy show or movie together. Or go for a nature walk on your own, meditate, do restorative yoga poses, or find a favorite creative hobby to relax. Relaxation breeds patience and helps quiet those strong but unhealthy compulsive behaviors.

MINDFULNESS TIPS:

- **Go Public:** To hold yourself accountable, tell friends and family your goal by posting it on FaceBook or Tweet about your challenges and successes. This will create a support system of people who will encourage you to stick with it. Research has shown positive encouragement and frequent reinforcement can substantially increase exercise compliance in people who were previously sedentary. Even exercisers who receive something so small as weekly encouragement via emails have greater success and better adherence to their wellness programs than those who opt to do it alone. Go public to help you be patient with plateaus and stay motivated to progress.

- **Acceptance Asanas:** Yoga is a life-long practice of patience: No matter how wise, strong, or flexible you are, there is always something more to learn, and refinement of yoga asanas (postures) requires years of practice. Learn to accept where you are on your yoga journey, and you will build patience. If you are impatient, you may strain to bring your nose to your knee in a forward bend, risking injury and missing out on the relaxation benefit. Instead, be content and grateful for what you *can* do; breathe and enjoy that space; and your body and mind just might release and expand into a deeper stretch. And remember that it's not just about perfecting the asanas: If it is, then your practice is solely for your ego and not your soul. Instead, develop your meditation skills and study the philosophy of yoga. Look for subtle changes in your breath, attitude, and how you view life. Take the patience and acceptance you learn in your yoga practice off the mat and into your life practice.

- **De-Tox Journal:** Journaling releases stress, which in turn can lower blood pressure, and have a positive affect on the immune system. Write about any toxic emotion (e.g., anger, guilt, jealousy, fear) you experienced in the past week, to allow you to see what you are feeling. *Why* did it affect you? Did it trigger a pain from the past? *How* did it affect you? Did it cause you to overeat or not follow your healthy intentions? If you did succeed where you failed in the past, write about how proud you were of being able to avoid an emotional outburst or unhealthy side effect. Explore the concept of perfection, and whether it drives you to toxic emotions. Would being perfect really change your life? Can you be content and **patient**, with full **acceptance** of where you are now, at this moment? Appreciate the journey. It's really all you have.

Journal

September

SEPTEMBER
Rituals and Routines

"Be where you are; otherwise you will miss your life."

BUDDHA

Summer is over, vacations have ended, and now it's back to school, work, and our normal routines. September (due to our early conditioning) is when many of us feel ready to make a fresh start, notch up our current fitness program, or try a different class. But just like when we were in school, before September is even gone we can find ourselves back in a rut and longing for another break.

Routines are necessary; they bring order, discipline, and purpose into our lives. Many routines, like going to work or school, we have done for a long time, so they have become rote habits. We tend to just go through the motions and lose connection to our daily actions, such as bathing, grooming, and even exercising. When we use the word "routine" as an adjective, we often mean the activity has become boring and tedious.

Take time this month to think about all the routines that make up your life. Do you smoke once or twice a day, but feel you're not addicted? Do you enjoy a daily glass of wine or cocktail, but think you could give it up at any point? Many of our daily practices are habitual and we associate times of day or other activities with these habits. Often, the hardest cigarette a smoker has to give up is the one she enjoys with her morning coffee, or the one she reaches for when drinking, as alcohol loosens inhibitions. It's hard to have one without the other. You may associate after-work relaxation with a glass of wine, when in fact a glass of sparkling water might illicit the same feeling over time, once your mind is conditioned to the new routine. Or try something entirely different and even healthier after work to relax, such as exercise or meditation every night at 5:00 PM. Be mindful of all your routines and contemplate which ones you wish to keep and which you could let go. What keeps some habits fresh, while others become stale? If you were to change your perspective, could these habits become less *routine*?

Rituals have been part of our ancestral history for thousands of years. They connect us to our past as we observe familial, cultural, and religious ceremonies. They also serve as reminders of where we have come from, and remind us that we are part of a whole universe of others past and present who shared the same customs. Like routines, rituals bring order and purpose into our lives, but they take it one step further. Rituals are a form of reverence; they bring honor and respect to a situation. In Japan, having a cup of tea is far from routine: The Japanese Tea Ceremony is an ancient ritual comprised of dozens of steps that represent harmony, respect, purity, and serenity. On a simpler level, your morning caffeine routine of rushing out the door with a commuter cup of coffee could be turned into a ritual: Take the time to savor the aroma and sip your fresh-brew from a cherished mug while observing the dawn sky fill with light.

Nature also has daily rituals – sunrise, sunset, high tide, low tide – that are constants in our life that we have come to depend on, and never tire of seeing. The cycles of the moon, weather, and seasons provide variety throughout the year, which helps us to appreciate and notice more. The animal kingdom's entire day consists of routines: feeding, grooming, and sleeping. Watch a bird take a bath, and notice the pleasure it receives as it splashes and hops around. Nature teaches us to be more present in our own lives, reminding us to find joy in our individual everyday routines.

Rituals are also an integral part of week-long destination spa stays or retreats. If you have had the opportunity to visit a spa or retreat site, recall the daily rituals you participated in. It may have been a sunrise hike, sunset meditation, short stroll after dinner, or the lighting a 15 to 20 minute meditation ritual at the same time each day, so your mind will be more willing to go deep inside and escape the outside chatter. Choose a realistic time that will work for you most days, and honor it as a well-needed spiritual retreat. Sing or learn to chant, and notice the sense of peace and happiness it brings to your soul. Revitalize the ritual of dressing each morning, and view the nurturing of your appearance as a sacred act. By treating your outer self as sacred, you celebrate the beauty within – your divine inner self.

- **Ritual Journal:** Some people believe they must journal daily and they do. But others fall victim to the "all-or-nothing" theory, so when they can't make it a daily routine, they stop writing. Instead, make journaling a one-day-per-week ritual. By giving yourself a choice, you may find yourself journaling other days because you *want* to, not because you *have* to. Create a symbolic statement of this special time for introspection by lighting a candle or sitting outdoors in the garden or by a window where you can observe nature. If you feel scattered and unfocused, beginning the day with your journal and a cup of your favorite coffee or tea will ground you. The newspaper, internet, and television will be there later. Instead, connect to the quiet of your personal world, while your mind is still unaffected by daily events. Reflect on your soul intentions: What feeds your soul, or what does your soul long for today? Let the words flow with your stream of conscious thoughts, forgetting about penmanship, spelling, or sentence structure. Remind yourself that the journal is for your eyes only, and resist the urge to judge, edit, or censor your work. Write about a favorite childhood ritual or compose a list of all the rituals you currently practice in your life. Choose the ritual that is most sacred to you, and write about it. Explore thoughts through the journaling process, and you may discover new **rituals** that will enrich your life and keep you on a life path of wellness.

SEP

JOURNAL

JOURNAL

October

OCTOBER
Ghosts of Your Past

"When you produce peace & happiness in yourself, you begin to realize peace for the whole world." THICH NHAT HANH

In the northern parts of the world, October is the month when deciduous trees display their fiery autumn finery of orange, yellow, and crimson. It is earth's last chance to impress us as it produces a grand finale of leaves before shutting down for the season. Like the trees, this is the time when we change our clothing, to prepare for the onset of cooler air, even for those of us who live in warmer climates. As we get our fall and winter wardrobe out of storage, it is a good time to re-examine last year's clothes to see what fits or is still in fashion. This year, ask yourself if your inner *and* outer lives still fit who you are now. Have you lost weight, but still hide behind baggy clothes? Are you afraid to show the world your new image? As nature changes its cloaks, so can we.

The tradition of Halloween is also in the air this month, which makes it an ideal time to observe the masks we may wear, and the fears that still haunt us. What ghosts of the past do you still fear? What masks do you wear? Do your masks hide a side of yourself you're afraid to show the world? Or do you hide behind beliefs of the past that may no longer fit who you are now? Does the fear of failure continually haunt you? Are you afraid of looking uncoordinated in a new class? Have you been avoiding an exercise or yoga pose because it spooks you? Break free and try that pose or exercise, with no fear of the outcome. Live life to the fullest instead of shutting down your dreams with fear. If you can learn to face your fears, you can move forward on your life path.

While the safety of complacency can be tempting (to avoid fearful situations), stepping out of your comfort zone can boost your mood and surprisingly, improve your health. Research has shown that when a risk taken produces positive results, we get a spike in dopamine, a chemical in the body that improves muscle movement, attention, and concentration. In addition, perceiving a fear as a challenge, rather than as a threat, can help the body and mind respond in a more positive and flexible way.

Most of us are familiar with the physiological benefits of strength training our muscles, but few people realize that it also confers self-empowerment benefits. Through the process of becoming physically strong, we build emotional strength. By resisting the urge to stop when the exercise gets hard (i.e., by doing those last couple challenging repetitions), we develop emotional *and* physical strength *and* willpower. Performing difficult exercises (or yoga poses) ignites *cognitive over-ride*, which is doing something your mind and body don't want to; that, in turn, builds tenacity and empowerment. We strengthen our mind the same way during meditation when we choose to over-ride the mindless chatter in our brains and replace it with breath focus. If strength training is not part of your current routine, start a program this month. You'll build your emotional strength, along with stronger bones and muscles.

As you savor the late-season sun and observe what's happening in nature, contemplate how your spiritual garden, or soul, has grown during the last 6 months. Have you given the seeds of intentions you sowed in the spring the tender loving care they needed to flourish? Just as a farmer learns from his crop each season, by making notes for next year to water less or fertilize more, we, too, can learn from our growth experience. For new habits to take root we may not need perfect conditions, but if we want something to grow, we must nurture it. What have you harvested from your life journey or your wellness and fitness program so far this year? Acknowledge and appreciate the healthy habits that have worked for you, and make time to enjoy the fruits of that harvest. Take note of the areas of opportunity you could fertilize and nurture to reap more rewards next season.

Be proud to display your finery by wearing clothes that complement your body and reflect who you are. Although it is most important to feel good inside, if we take care in how we present ourselves, we are not only respecting others but showing self-respect, which helps build a positive self-image. Keep in mind that some of us may have the tendency to become obsessed with portraying a perfect image, whereas others don't care enough and appear sloppy or unkempt. Strive for a balance of the two extremes. As you dress, appreciate what you see in the mirror, and accept your own beauty and worth.

October is the time to harvest – to acknowledge and enjoy – the healthy and fit body, mind, and spirit you have produced as a result of your efforts over the past seasons. Even if you are just beginning a wellness program, appreciate all your body *can* do. Celebrate the past and its lessons that have brought you to where you are today. Unmask your fears, and leave the **ghosts of your past** behind. Live freely in the now, as you make a plan to move mindfully toward the future you aspire to.

FITNESS TIPS:

- **Why Weight?:** If strength training is not currently part of your exercise routine, start lifting weights this month: Your muscles can't "weight." Around age 40, women begin to lose muscle (lean body mass) at a faster rate. A strength training program will maintain and increase muscle mass, which is vital for functional health and ease of daily living, in addition to improving bone density, balance, and muscle tone. Having a higher lean-body-mass-to-fat-mass ratio burns more calories even while sitting, so it is an important aide to metabolism and weight loss as well. The American College of Sports Medicine (ACSM) recommends strength training all the major muscles of the body 2 or 3 nonconsecutive days per week. A program of 8 to 10 exercises performed in 1 to 3 sets using a weight you can lift 8 to 12 reps is suggested for most women interested in general fitness and muscle and bone strength. Effective methods can include (or combine) strength training machines, free weights (dumbbells or barbells), body weight only, or resistance bands or tubes; what's most important is that the effort is challenging enough that 12 reps in a row is the *maximum* that can be performed. Once 12 reps can be executed with ease, it is then time to increase the weight or resistance. For maximum results, perform 2 to 3 sets of each exercise, resting 20 to 30 seconds in between each one.

- **Ghost-Busters:** If strength exercises spook you, hire a personal trainer to design a fitness program tailored to your specific goals, ability, and medical history. A trainer will teach you good form and help you avoid injury while increasing your chance of success. Ask friends who have had positive results with a trainer for recommendations. Besides education and certification, experience is of equal importance when choosing a trainer. And professionalism and personality should also be considered. Pick someone you feel comfortable with who listens intently to your needs and concerns. To help you feel emotionally and physically strong, consider joining a boxing, martial arts, or fencing class, or hire a personal coach to teach you empowering skills that will "ghost-bust" your fears away.

- **Progress Pride:** Strengthen your intentions and develop pride in your progress; this will help you stay motivated throughout the upcoming holidays. Are you lifting heavier weights, walking, or running farther or faster than you were several months ago? Or maybe you are finally following a program, taking a yoga class, being consistent. Reflect on and record all that you have harvested from your efforts, and be both proud and grateful. If you have nothing to harvest because you did not stay with your exercise plan, think about any attempts you made, your past history, and why you weren't successful. Are there ghosts in your past still hanging on, voices telling you you're just going to fail again, or that you've always been chubby or un-athletic, so who are you trying to fool? Perhaps you have been masquerading as someone else (wearing a dated self-image) but that is not who you are anymore, it's just a feeling you still have. Discard your mask and stand up to those ghosts. Increase your chance of success by envisioning a more positive and fitter you, by exercising and following your intentions.

HEALTHY EATING TIPS:

- **Carb Fright:** Do you suffer from "carb fright?" Do you avoid bread, cereal, and even fruit, out of worry that all carbs make you fat? Have no fear: Healthy unrefined carbs are the best fuel source for exercise, because they are quickly converted into energy. Avoid refined or "bad carbs," like baked goods, sweets, and refined grains, which have zero nutritional benefit and give you a rush of sugar high, followed by a quick crash. Instead, go for "good" carbs, like whole grains, beans, fruits, vegetables, and low-fat dairy. But keep in mind that excess calories of *any* kind of food add up to weight gain and be mindful of portion sizes.

- **Weight Loss Won't Make You Happy:** Some people are under the mistaken assumption that once they achieve their weight loss goals, they will live happily ever after; they incorrectly believe all their problems are a result of being overweight. ("If I could just lose these ten pounds…") Once they realize that life is fundamentally the same after weight loss, this kind of thinking can lead to a return to former eating habits and eventual weight regain. To prevent this from happening to you, don't allow your happiness to be contingent on whether your weight is exactly where you think it should be, or whether you've achieved all your fitness and wellness goals. Be in the now. Accept and appreciate all your body does for you today, and stay with your intentions that will guide your body to a healthier state.

- **Trick or Treat:** The Academy of Nutrition & Dietetics (formally called the American Dietetic Association) suggests limiting added sugar intake to 8 teaspoons (32 grams) per day. (A typical 12-ounce can of cola contains 39 grams.) If you have a sweet tooth, Halloween can be a tricky time of year: To prevent bingeing, buy only healthy treats or toys to give out to trick-or-treaters and stay away from your own kids' bags! If you *are* able to stop at one treat, allow yourself to enjoy one favorite candy bar (preferably snack-size) from your childhood: Treat yourself guilt-free. One sugary treat on one day is not going to set you back (if it *is* just one day). But don't be tricked into thinking you're in the clear if you go on a binge and don't gain weight immediately. It takes time for the metabolism to catch up; the body has a sneaky way of adjusting to increased calories, so you may be spooked when you see the scale in the weeks to follow.

Mindfulness Tips:

- **Mirror Mask:** Have you ever taken an exercise class and found the section of mirror that made you look the slimmest? Or gone to a Fun House of Mirrors? Think of how those images affected how you felt about yourself. Look in the mirror, and notice any positive changes in your body shape and musculature since you started eating and exercising healthfully. *Can* you see the changes in your image, or do you still see the ghost of your past? Some people who lose a lot of weight still see themselves as that large person, and even avoid small spaces they wouldn't have been able to squeeze through before. If you avoid full-length mirrors because you know you've gained weight and are afraid to face the reality, continuing this practice could cause you to gain even more weight. Instead, face your fear and gaze at your image, and see yourself as you really are now.

- **Micro-Meditate:** Daily meditation has been proven to decrease blood pressure, increase brain power, and improve sleep. If you're not currently meditating, and just can't imagine finding the time to sit still for 15 to 30 minutes, try small doses. Use a free iPhone app called "Chakra Chime" to create a more ritualistic element to your meditation session. Set the app for any amount of minutes, and three relaxing chimes will ring to signal the end. Practice mini-meditations 2 to 3 times per day for 3 to 10 minutes. Close your eyes and imagine that your eyelids are like shades on your windows to the world, and for just a few minutes you can take refuge and focus on your inner world. Or, rather than just meditating for minutes, try immersing yourself all day in mindfulness meditation by being present in each moment, and discover the peace and tranquility inside you that is available to you 24/7.

- **Ghost-Buster Journal:** Fear can be disguised as anger, jealousy, greed, or ego attachment. When there is absence of love for oneself, or if we don't feel whole, fear (or one of its disguises) is present. Do you see your future through the lens of fear? The lens of fear distorts what you see, often exaggerating, and focusing on the negative. Most fears are unfounded, yet they force you to compromise your core values by putting you in a survival mode. Compose a list of fears you've had in the past. Check the ones that came true, cross off the ones that didn't, and circle the ones that are still present. Take the time to confront any ghosts of your past head-on by journaling about them. Who are you masquerading as, and has your mask evolved from your fears? Are you trying to trick yourself or others? Seeing your fears and doubts written down in black and white lets you evaluate the actual risks, and help vaporize them. It's never too late to journal about a past traumatic experience that you may have muscled through and not let go of. Writing brings the trauma out of the dark and into the light, allowing you to acknowledge and understand what happened, to help heal emotional wounds and see yourself as a survivor rather than a victim. By appreciating all it took to move on, you will leave your haunted house and any **ghosts of your past** behind.

JOURNAL

November

NOVEMBER
(Don't) Fall Back

"Life can only be understood backward, but it must be lived forward." Soren Kierkegaard

In most parts of the country November is the month when we set our clocks back to standard time. As the daylight diminishes, our intentions can also become dimmer as we are tempted to eat more, stay inside, and move less. It is easy to **fall back** to unhealthy patterns. This year, instead of reverting back to old ways, cultivate an attitude of gratitude; see how making this choice can help you stay focused on a forward path, not just this month, but all year round. Studies have found that people who kept a gratitude journal and listed five things they were grateful for once a week for two months tend to be more optimistic, have fewer physical problems, and spend more time working out. As Thanksgiving approaches reflect daily on all you are grateful for. In addition to the obvious (e.g., your health, spouse, family, friends, work, and home), recall the simple joys of nature, a kind act of a stranger or friend, or a new insight. Think back on and record all that you have learned in the past year, and how those twists and turns have led you to where you are today. Envisioning the big picture (even when it's not possible to see the good) gives us faith that one day we will see how it moved us forward on our path. Seeing the wisdom gained when something disappointing or even bad happens is an example of expressing gratitude. And gratitude is one of the most important ingredients needed to develop inner joy.

The shorter days this month can affect even the most positive person's attitude. If you live in the North and the thought of the long winter ahead depresses you, book a tropical February vacation now or schedule a winter visit to spend time with a friend you don't often see. These events could become annual winter traditions that you look forward to. If you experience SAD (seasonal affective disorder), consider taking up an outdoor sport or plan walks as often as possible to enjoy the positive effects of the natural light and the fresh air that nature has to offer.

When the days turn dark earlier, we tend to isolate ourselves more. For those who live alone, don't work outside the home, or who lack regular social connections, the winter months can be the loneliest time of the year. Studies have shown that social isolation not only affects our well-being, but can also directly affect longevity, greatly increasing a woman's risk of heart disease. Conversely, strong social support can help lower blood pressure and improve other cardiovascular functions. If you find yourself spending most of your days alone, schedule weekly walking dates with a friend or meet for a meal or drink. Join a book club or a volunteer group. Take a yoga or fitness class: Interactions with like-minded people in a class (even if no words are exchanged) are extremely therapeutic, both physically and psychologically.

Our frenetic lifestyles can cause us to seek more solitary time at home during winter, ignoring our neighbors and eating in more often. Many people turn to Facebook and other social networking sites, rather than meeting friends face-to-face. And if we do meet people in person and they spend time sending text messages while we are talking, we are deprived of a genuine experience. Make an effort to reconnect in person with friends, and ask everyone to disconnect from electronic devices, so you can feel the psychological comfort that comes from being fully present and engaged with another human being. We are all guilty of multi-tasking while talking on the phone with friends and family. Whenever possible, avoid multi-tasking, and give callers your undivided attention. They will benefit from your full presence, and you will notice the relaxing effect a truly conscious social connection has when you return to your tasks after your call.

While some of us have too much time alone, others don't have enough. Lack of solitary time causes stress levels to rise and can make us frustrated, irritated, and edgy. And as we spend less time in the wide open space of the great outdoors, and more time indoors, these feelings can magnify as the space around us begins to feel smaller. The relationships we have – with our spouse, family, and friends – are the most valuable assets of our lives. It's important to designate quality time for them, but also for yourself: Schedule at least 30 minutes a day of complete privacy and alone time, just for you, to feed your soul.

In this month of Thanksgiving, acknowledge abundance and the rich harvests that shape this season. To keep you from feeling down, appreciate what you do have, all the goodness in your life, and harvest the time that is available to you. Practicing gratitude paves the way to developing inner joy. Be grateful for your family and friends, and for your health; and make time for all of them, including yourself, so you **don't fall back**.

FITNESS TIPS:

- **Fall Prevention:** Balance exercises (along with strength training) help prevent falls and injuries. A simple at-home routine to do daily could include heel-to-toe walking (like walking on a curb); single-leg balance (standing on one leg); and heel and toe raises (without holding on to anything for balance). When balancing, if your body sways and moves, it's part of the learning process (brain-training) in which the brain is trying to find the body's center. To build hip and spinal bone density (along with agility), hop from foot-to-foot (side-to-side) 100 times, or jump rope. (If you have back or knee injuries, advanced osteoporosis, or experience pain with impact, skip the jumps.)

- **48-Hour Rule:** Remember that the heart is a muscle, too! Just as you shouldn't strength train the same muscle groups 2 days in a row, avoid consecutive high-intensity or strenuous cardio workouts as well. Alternate with lower-intensity workouts to give your heart and body a chance to recover and build strength, just like when you weight train. If you practice power yoga, consider alternating with a softer style or restorative yoga.

- **MAXimize Your Cardio:** Do you frequently fall back on the same mindless cardio workouts? It's time to rev up your metabolism! If you have been consistent with your cardio workouts for at least 6 months, maximize the calorie-and-fat-burning effects of your cardio by performing interval workouts two times per week: Warm up at a moderate intensity for 10 minutes, then perform multiple bouts of high-intensity cardio, alternating with low-intensity cardio recovery intervals for a total of 20 to 30 minutes, finishing with a 5-minute cooldown. The shorter the interval, the higher the intensity. The ratio of hard to easy intervals can be the same time amount, or you can reduce or double the easy intervals if you need less or more recovery. For example: 2 to 4 minutes hard followed by 1 to 2 minutes easy recovery (5 to 10 bouts). Or 30 seconds very hard, followed by 30 to 60 seconds easy (10 to 20 bouts).

Healthy Eating Tips:

- **Don't Fall Back:** When the weather turns cooler, salads and light meals can lose their appeal, and it can be tempting to fall back on old favorites that are high in fat and calories. Avoid temptation by doing as spa chefs do: Cut fat and sugar in soups, sauces, and desserts by substituting non-fat evaporated milk for cream; non-fat plain Greek yogurt for butter or cream cheese; phyllo dough for pastry crust; and pureed fruits for sugar. And consider this: To avoid falling back to the same foods, try something new this month (like an unfamiliar ethnic food or spice), or retry a food you used to dislike. Experts in food neophobia (the fear of new food) say that it takes five to ten attempts at trying something before you reach the point where you don't reject it outright. Just as we can alter our brain chemistry by eating more and more sweeter foods, we can – with practice and an open mind – alter our brain to respond more positively to bitter, healthier foods such as kale, turnip, and cranberries. Challenge (and please) your palate with a variety of textures and a balance of tastes (sour, bitter, salty and sweet) in every meal. Train your taste buds and try one new dish per week, and you are sure to discover some healthy *and* tasty winners.

- **Micro Meals:** Instead of three big meals, eat five mini meals daily. Think kid's size. Your metabolism is like a wood stove: If you don't feed it, the fire will go out. Not fueling your body regularly by waiting 4 hours or more to eat confuses your body. It doesn't know when it's going to get fed next, and automatically slows down its metabolism, so you burn fewer calories. As part of your five mini meals, include a protein snack (low-fat cheese, almonds, or an egg) at 3 to 4 PM. This balances blood sugar levels, which prevents insulin levels from rising. (Insulin is what makes you store fat around the middle.) If you don't eat enough lunch and skip this protein snack, insulin levels will rise, increasing your risk of developing belly fat. Be sure to eat *small* snacks (100 to 150 calories each) every few hours to keep blood sugar, energy, and mood on an even keel.

- **Fall for Orange:** Focus on all the richly colored fall vegetables and fruits that are in season right now: Think pumpkins, butternut squashes, and sweet potatoes, in addition to tangerines, kumquats, and persimmons. Aim for at least one serving per day of something orange to ensure a healthy dose of beta-carotene and other important nutrients. The antioxidants that are found in brightly colored produce have a short shelf-life in our bodies. We can't store them for long, so it's best to include one serving of a brightly colored vegetable or fruit with each meal.

Mindfulness Tips:

- **Nature Immersion:** Spend time in nature, and get back to basics. To avoid getting caught up in the commercialism and pressure of the upcoming holidays, practice appreciation and gratitude for what is truly important now, to make it easier to stick with it next month, when the days get even shorter and perhaps colder. Nature can be the best teacher of mindfulness. Even if you live in a big city, there is much to see, and so much that can be missed. Notice how different the light looks in late afternoon, noting the shadows and the softness. Enjoy the peak daylight sun now that the harsh intensity of the summer sun is gone. Feel the change in the air (e.g., the temperature, the dryness, or the humidity, depending on where you live) and appreciate the variation. Watch the animal kingdom preparing for a new season: The squirrels gathering and storing nuts, birds flying south, or hawks circling high above.

- **Sabotage Prevention:** If there is a person in your life who has sabotaged your healthy lifestyle efforts in the past, prepare a plan to avoid falling prey to that situation again. Reinforce your feelings, and strengthen your intentions: Write the words you wish to say to that person, and visualize yourself succeeding. If you can anticipate a likely sabotage attempt, and have an action plan or script to counteract it, you will be less likely to fall back. If in the past you felt your diet was sabotaged by your annual Thanksgiving Day hosts, offer to bring a healthy side dish this year. At the holiday table, fill half your plate with the healthiest low-fat foods, and take polite small portions of the richer high-fat specialties of your host. And eat slowly so you won't be offered seconds.

- **Gratitude Journal:** Take this month of Thanksgiving to create a daily ritual of thanks for your blessings. At the end of each day, write down at least one thing you are grateful for. Writing gratitude thoughts down (as opposed to just thinking them) causes crystallization, allowing a deeper penetration to the subconscious. If you already keep a regular journal, write your gratitude entries in the back of the book or keep a separate gratitude journal. Place it on your night stand, and recall and record what you are grateful for before you go to sleep. If troubles come into your mind during the night, recall and focus on what you wrote. In the morning, read your entry from the previous evening, and give thanks for another day. To prevent **fall back,** develop an attitude of gratitude. Take time to recognize and appreciate the good in yourself and your life, and how far you've come – and you will continue to move *forward* on your life path.

NOV

Journal

December

DECEMBER
Guilt-Free Choices

"Peace does not mean to be in a place where there is no noise, trouble or hard work. It means to be in the midst of those things and still be calm in your heart."

December marks the end of the calendar year and the beginning of winter. It is also the month that can feel like an endless celebration of the holidays, with food and drink almost always present. While some of us look forward to this month with joyful anticipation, others just feel dread. This dread can be due to the lack of time to accomplish all that needs to be done or having to face dysfunctional family members or feeling alone with no one to celebrate with. Even for those of us who love the holidays, this month presents challenges and time constraints that can threaten our relationships and our health – causing our stress levels to light up like a Christmas tree. December is a month chock full of choices. We face the challenges of choosing whether to exercise, or to give in to holiday cheer. Sometimes we really do have no choice in the matter, but other times it can be just our habitual way of thinking that rules us. Our wellness traditions are not as deep-rooted as our holiday rituals, so we tend to do what we've always done, or what's expected of us. Many of the choices we make this month are driven by guilt. We can feel guilty for over-indulging when we cave in and drink our friend's homemade eggnog and just as guilty if we don't, for fear of causing hurt feelings. We can feel guilty when we don't go to the gym and guilty when we do if we have deprived our family of a holiday routine in order to squeeze in a workout. And then there is the guilt over all we may possess; our ability to give gifts to our children or to throw a party, while others struggle to even put food on the table, can also be a source of holiday anxiety. If the season itself is the reason for your stress, consider how you could stay in balance *this* year by making **guilt-free choices**.

The frenetic consumerism that assaults us during December can cause us to feel we aren't giving enough or doing enough of the traditional things we associate with the holidays. Are you susceptible to activity addiction? The ego gets addicted to being busy and soon you need more and more hits to get that original high. If you have to skip a workout or yoga practice due to a holiday activity, question exactly what needs to be done now, what can be done another time, or if it is really needed at all. Are you doing this out of habit, because you think you *should*, or because it's truly important to you? Consider new holiday rituals that might require less work or be healthier in nature. Ask your family what traditions are most important to them. (You just might be surprised by their answers.) On the other hand, is your exercise addiction not allowing you to take time out to do holiday preparations or to experience the merriment? Assuming you're not a pro athlete in training for a competition, letting up on some of the hours you put in at the gym this month won't set you back. In fact, your body might just get stronger if you give it a little more of the recovery time it deserves. And keep in mind that both exercise and activity addictions are not just December afflictions.

We wish each other peace and joy for the holidays, and we may sing well-known Christmas carols with lyrics claiming "all is calm," and "sleep in heavenly peace." Reflect on what the words "peace" and "calm" mean to you, and how you might bring those qualities into your life more often. When we are calm, we can focus better, and therefore accomplish more in less time. Only when we are content with who we are, what we have, and where we are in life can we enjoy true peace. The practice of gratitude is the way to contentment. If you feel discontented with what you are able to do for the holidays – whether it is due to lack of time, money, or family – accept your current reality and be grateful for what you *can* do. If you don't observe Christmas due to differing religious or personal beliefs, consider starting an annual ritual of your own to fill the void you feel when everyone else seems to be celebrating. Throw a winter solstice party or plan a picnic to show your gratitude for the cycles of nature, the variety and rituals it offers, the beauty of the changing light. Increase your awareness, which will allow you to see and appreciate more. Reaffirm what is truly important this season – the people in your life, nature, and your health. Think about the contentment you felt after taking 10 glorious minutes outdoors to let the sunbeams warm your face or your child's joy when you took him to see Santa, even though it meant standing in line for 20 minutes and missing your yoga class. Stay mindful, and you will be able to find the positive side of each situation. In time, this will create more contentment, calmness, and peace in your life. You *do* have a choice: Create calmness out of chaos.

Challenge yourself during this season of giving to be present in your thoughts: Think twice before choosing how to make best use of your time or what to give to others, so you can retain some semblance of your wellness routine and maintain balance. And since it is the holidays, celebrate and enjoy the season – **guilt-free** – with the **choices** you do make. December also marks the transition from fall to winter, and the transition from the end of one year to the beginning of another. It's a time to reflect and give thanks for what you have reaped the past four seasons, as you move mindfully into the blank canvas of a new year, leading – if you choose – to a calmer and more joyful you.

FITNESS TIPS:

- **Shopping Circuit:** When shopping or running errands, park far away and walk as much as possible; extending your route by going to the store farthest away first, or making a few laps back and forth in the mall. At the grocery store, shop the perimeter of the store, where the healthier foods are displayed and if possible avoid the interior aisles, so you won't be tempted by unhealthy snacks and sweets. Carry your shopping bags to increase your calorie-burning, and speed walk between stores. Just 10 minutes of brisk walking can increase your energy for 2 hours. Do heel and toe raises, balance exercises, and stretches while standing in the checkout line. While wrapping gifts, stand at a countertop instead of sitting at a table. Make mindful choices to move more, which will all add up to more calories burned at the end of the day.

- **Say No to All-or-Nothing Thinking:** Do *what* you can *when* you can. No one has a perfect workout week all the time. Be realistic during the holiday season. Aim for 6 days of exercise per week, so that if plans get derailed due to unexpected events, you are guaranteed at least a minimum of 3 days. *But,* if that strategy makes you feel guilty for not working out 6 days, plan on only three sessions. And if you don't have time for your normal workout or yoga practice, just do a few exercises or yoga poses. Twenty, or even 10 minutes are better than none. If three exercise sessions per week this month is an impossibility, do not abandon your program until January! Choose instead to attend at least one class or training session per week so you can maintain your fitness level, as well as the connection to your routine. And be as active as you can in between workouts.

- **Train Your Whole Body:** The body works as a whole, so focus on training it that way. Forget spot reducing. The most effective exercises are functional in nature and designed for how the body moves in real life, incorporating several groups of muscles at once. If you can't get to the gym, challenge yourself with these functional multi-joint choices that maximize your time and require no equipment:

  1. **Sit-to-Stand Squats:** Stand in front of a sturdy chair with arms crossed over chest. Move hips back, keeping knees over toes, and slowly lower to touch chair

seat and rise back up, squeezing buttocks and pressing down through heels. Perform 15 to 20 reps.

2. **Push-Ups:** (Straight leg on toes, modified on knees, or at countertop.) Place hands on floor or countertop a little wider than shoulder-width apart, arms straight. Maintaining neutral spine, bend elbows and lower chest/body as one unit to floor or toward counter, then push back up to start. Perform 15 to 20 reps.

3. **Alternating Single-Leg Dead Lifts:** Bend forward from waist with a flat, straight spine, reaching both hands to floor as you lift one leg behind you *simultaneously*; then rise up and repeat with other leg. Perform 10 reps each leg.

4. **Plank:** Lie on floor, face down, legs straight. Prop yourself up to forearms with elbows below shoulders. Rise up to toes and hold, maintaining neutral spine (as in a push-up). (If too difficult, drop knees to floor.) Hold for 30 to 60 seconds.

5. **Alternating Elbow to Opposite Knee Bicycle Crunches:** Lie on back with feet off floor, knees bent over hips, hands interlocked behind head. Draw right knee in toward chest as you straighten left leg, lowering it toward floor while raising shoulder blades off floor and bringing left shoulder toward right knee. Repeat opposite side. Keep motion smooth and controlled. Perform 15 reps each side.

HEALTHY EATING TIPS:

- **Splurge Strategy:** Plan ahead for splurges so you can avoid feeling deprived and enjoy the holidays like everyone else. Choose one or two occasions (parties, holidays, cookie-baking, etc) you will splurge each week, but limit the splurge to a single meal, party, or baking day testing. Just eat a little less than usual on non-splurge days.

Don't skip meals, stick with your regular schedule, but make healthy lower-calorie choices. And exercise a minimum of three times per week, so the spurges won't cause weight gain. Remember, it's not what you eat between Thanksgiving and New Year's: It's what you eat between New Year's and Thanksgiving that counts the most.

- **Select and Savor:** To avoid overeating at a party, never arrive hungry. When you have a choice at dinner parties, decide which treat you really want, and take small portions of those less-healthy options, filling your plate with salad and veggies. And enjoy every mindful bite of the treat you choose *guilt-free*.

- **Rethink That Drink:** If you choose to drink alcohol, sip slowly and mindfully, so you really taste and enjoy your drink. And limit yourself: Liquid calories add up quickly and increase your appetite, while reducing your willpower. Additionally, studies have shown that alcohol consumption increases the propensity to store fat around the middle. Beware of hostesses or servers who constantly top off your wine glass, making it difficult to assess how much you've really consumed. A simple hand gesture over your glass will alert them from over-pouring. Alternate sparkling water with each glass of wine or mixed drink you consume. In your own home, serve guests special appealing non-alcoholic cocktails, such as sparkling water with a splash of pomegranate juice and a raspberry or two in a pretty champagne glass.

MINDFULNESS TIPS:

- **All is Calm:** Find small ways to de-stress throughout each day during the holiday season. Even a 5-minute walk outdoors can be restorative if you allow yourself to focus on nature and not your shopping list. Regardless of whether you are in the country or the city, notice the sights and sounds that surround you, to remind you to feel and be aware. In this hectic season as we rush around and lose control of our time, our ability to be aware and sense our feelings also diminishes. When we are not aware, it's harder to *be*ware, and we make unhealthy choices. Our breath is one thing we can control. In addition to lowering heart rate and blood pressure, meditating on breath offers a sense of control over your emotions that is extremely therapeutic. Take deep breaths often, especially when stuck in traffic or long lines, to erase anxiety and calm the mind. Say to yourself "in and out" as you notice your inhalation and exhalation. Breath focus during exercise routines will teach you how to relax during stressful times in your life. When you feel tension while performing an exercise or yoga pose and want to hold your breath, take a deep breath instead, and release and feel the calmness that comes with the exhale.

- **Embrace Tradition:** Holiday traditions are part of our culture. Some have become commercialized, while others remain meaningful. Have your holiday traditions become routine? Make them feel like rituals again by preparing special dinners or cookies mindfully and with love. By following a tradition a beloved or departed family member once embraced, it will connect you to them as you honor their memory; it can also be a source of comfort if you mourn their loss this holiday month. Engage in traditions related to your religion or beliefs to embrace the true meaning of the season.

- **Guilt-Free Journal:** Generosity can feel like something that is expected of us at this time of year. Think about all you give to others and what you receive back. How does it feel to be generous with your time, as you do things for others to make them happy? Can you give gifts with no expectation of receiving one back? Can you receive gifts with grace and no guilt if you didn't give one? Guilt is a toxic emotion that many women experience far too often and in many cases, unnecessarily, brought on by their own minds or past ways of thinking. Writing about any guilt you feel can help you understand its true origin, and if it is unfounded, free your mind of it. Journal about a holiday-related guilt you experience, from overeating to overspending. Write about **choices** you are forced to make and how that makes you feel. Be sure to also include positive entries about how empowering it is to make new choices and to feel **guilt-free** or how your family supports you and responds to your choices. And journal about a calm or peaceful moment or day that you experienced, a favorite holiday memory from the past, or the tradition that brings you the most joy. Find a way to hold onto that experience and joy as you move forward on your life path into a new year.

DEC

JOURNAL

Journal

ACKNOWLEDGEMENTS
& GRATITUDE

With reverent appreciation for all my past and present teachers and students, for all they have taught me, and for all they continue to inspire in me.

For my talented book designer, Teri Rider, who patiently and cheerfully coached me through the gestation period of this creative project.

For my editor, Diane Lofshult, for her professional advice and knowledge of the subject matter, as well as her expertise in the editing process.

For Francine Hoffman, Inner Focus coordinator at Golden Door, and trusted friend and yoga mentor, for her faith in my abilities and her continual support of my development as a yoga teacher.

For Trish Martin, Fitness Supervisor at Golden Door, for her help and support of my desire to pursue the mindfulness field, by giving me the opportunity to teach journaling and yoga classes.

For my dear friend, L, for all the time she took to read, review, and critique my manuscripts over and over, and for her expert photography tips, insight, and compassion for the entire project.

For my parents, Ken & Dot, for their unconditional love and guidance, and for their encouragement to go outside and play, which instilled in me an early connection to nature. Because of their influence I found joy and appreciation in experiences, rather than material things.

For my husband, David, for recognizing and respecting my need and passion to write, even when it cut into our precious time together, for his willingness to read and edit my drafts, and for being the one to say "just write."

ACTIVITY LOG

WEEK OF:_____Weight: Monday:_____ Friday:_____

Record specific activities and duration of exercises performed, and any mindfulness (meditation, time in nature, creative arts, etc.) practiced:

MONDAY

Cardio: _____

Strength/Stability/Flexibility: _____

Mindfulness: _____

TUESDAY

Cardio: _____

Strength/Stability/Flexibility: _____

Mindfulness: _____

WEDNESDAY

Cardio: _____

Strength/Stability/Flexibility:_____

Mindfulness:_____

Thursday

Cardio: _____

Strength/Stability/Flexibility: _____

Mindfulness: _____

Friday

Cardio: _____

Strength/Stability/Flexibility: _____

Mindfulness: _____

Saturday

Cardio: _____

Strength/Stability/Flexibility: _____

Mindfulness: _____

Sunday

Cardio: _____

Strength/Stability/Flexibility: _____

Mindfulness: _____

HEALTHY EATING JOURNAL

WEEK OF:_____Weight: Monday:_____ Friday:_____

Record food intake, calories, and/or mindfulness observed:

Monday: _____

_____

_____

_____

_____

_____

Tuesday: _____

_____

_____

_____

_____

_____

Wednesday: _____

_____

_____

_____

_____

_____

Thursday: _____

_____

_____

_____

_____

_____

Friday: _____

_____

_____

_____

_____

_____

Saturday: _____

_____

_____

_____

_____

_____

Sunday: _____

_____

_____

_____

_____

"The future is not someplace we are going to, but a place we are creating. The paths to it are not found, they are made."

JOHN SCHAAR